THE BIG VIZ BOOK OF ADVENTURE

WRITTEN BY
GRAHAM DURY & SIMON THORP

ILLUSTRATED BY
SIMON ECOB

ADDITIONAL ILLUSTRATIONS BY SIMON THORP AND GRAHAM DURY

ADDITIONAL MATERIAL BY GUY CAMPBELL, ALEX COLLIER, CHRIS DONALD, SIMON DONALD, DAVEY JONES AND TED THORNHILL

Published by Dennis Publishing Ltd
30 Cleveland Street, London W1T 4JD

ISBN 9 781781 063712
First Printing Autumn 2014

Printed in the United Kingdom

Subscribe online at www.viz.co.uk

MILLIONS of us buy a newspaper every day to keep us abreast of what's going on in the world. We read them and we throw them away, but who amongst us ever stops to think about how they are produced? Let's take a look behind the headlines at a typical day in the life of a newspaper.

THE STORY of your morning paper starts a whole 24 hours before it hits the streets, when an editorial meeting is held. Stories may come from many sources; press agencies at home and abroad; correspondents filing eye-witness reports from war-zones around the globe; investigative journalists doggedly pursuing tip-offs and leads. Here the editor and his staff go through the early editions of their rival papers looking for stories about celebrities to rip off.

BACK IN the pub, the journalist manages to snatch a few seconds between trebles for a quick sandwich and six bags of crisps. Then it's back to work, leaning on the bar spouting opinionated libellous gossip to anyone who'll listen.

IT IS the job of the campaigning journalist to expose injustice and root out corruption in high places. Woodward and Bernstein's Watergate cover-up story was responsible for bringing down a president, whilst John Pilger's fearless reporting has led to the exposure of many human rights abuses. Here, an investigative journalist with a hidden camera is being wanked off in a massage parlour by a woman in suspenders.

HIS HEART attack over, our reporter is racing against time. There are only thirty minutes left before his copy must be on the sub-editor's desk, but circumstances are conspiring against him - the business desk of the Financial Times has just come in and they're six deep at the bar.

JOURNALISM, as with many professions, has its less enjoyable sides. Here, a junior reporter has been threatened with the sack unless he 'doorsteps' a recently bereaved mother in order to suggest that her son died of AIDS. It's a job that requires sensitivity, tact and nimble fingers to pocket a school photograph from the mantelpiece.

ONCE the story has been decided upon, it is assigned to a reporter. Deadlines are tight and he knows there is no time to lose. Within seconds he's in the pub guzzling trebles and fiddling his expenses.

NEWSPAPERS not only inform, they also make us laugh. It is the job of the editorial cartoonist to take a humorous look at one of the day's stories. Here we see the artist hard at work. His caricatures are instantly recognisable as, with a few deft lines from his pen, he writes who it is supposed to be on their shirt.

IN THE PUB, it's 2.30 and time for a heart attack.

IN THE WORLD of newspapers, a picture is worth a thousand words. Don McCullin's harrowing photographs have been credited with hastening the end of the Vietnam war. This gin-soaked old smudger, however, is up a tree in the South of France trying to get a picture of Posh Spice's tits.

WITH JUST seconds to go, the story is finally filed. It is now the job of the sub-editor to change the facts and quotes made up by the reporter, in order to suit an amusing punny headline that he thought of earlier that morning.

9.00PM and the editor finally 'puts the paper to bed'. The presses start rolling, printing the first of millions of copies that will find their way onto our breakfast tables. For the printers, there is a long evening's work ahead. For the journalists, there is just enough time to nip to the pub all night before the whole dismal process starts again the next morning.

Jack Black & his dog Silver in the **MYSTERY OF THE SHORTBREAD & LONG TROUSERS**

Jack Black and his dog Silver stepped onto the station platform near the remote Northumbrian village of Embleton-on-the-Wall. It was Spring half term at last, and they were going to spend it here with Aunt Meg in her converted Kentish oasthouse.

Hello, Aunt Meg!

Hello, young Jack!

Let's get you two home. You'll be wanting a nice hot bath after your long journey.

You can say that again

Shortly...

My, you have grown, Jack. Now, have you washed down on the farm?

Yes

Have you cleaned inside the farmer's hat?

Yes, Aunt Meg.

Come on then. Let's get you dry.

Wait a minute!...

...what are these little hairs around my tassel?

Bless you, Jack. They're called pubes. They're nothing to worry about, just a sign that you're turning from a boy into a young gentleman.

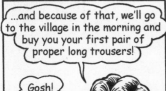

...and because of that, we'll go to the village in the morning and buy you your first pair of proper long trousers!

Gosh! Really!?

Woof!

That evening, Jack was so excited he found it hard to get to sleep, and spent the whole night tossing in his bed...

Bright and early the next morning, Meg, Jack and Silver arrived in Embleton-on-the-Wall.

E. W. POOLE GENTS OUTFITTERS

Hello Mr. Poole. I'd like some long trousers for my nephew, Jack. It's his first pair.

Goodness. Pubes around his dicky mint already is it, Meg?

That's right, Mr Poole.

Ah! Don't they grow up quickly these days...

But I'm afraid my entire stock of long trousers has been stolen....

What!?

I don't understand it, Meg, really I don't.

But who on earth would want so many trousers, Mr. Poole?

I don't know, Jack. PC Brown is baffled. The only clue he could find was a few biscuit crumbs by the broken window...

...it's all very mysterious!

It *was* all very mysterious, but as they left the shop, they saw something which puzzled them even more...

Morning, Meg. ...Jack.

P.C. Brown!! What the...!?

Ah, yes. I'm sorry about this rather unusual attire. I had to borrow some of my wife's clothing...

...only my police trousers have been stolen off the washing line at the station.

Well, what a funny old day it's turning out to be, Jack...

NORTHUMBERLAND LINGERIE

Trousers... crumbs... it doesn't add up!

REDPATH GROCERS

BROKEN SHORTBREAD
-large tins-
NOW HALF PRICE!!

...first of all there are no trousers in the shop and then the village bobby turns up in his wife's underwear... whatever next...?

His mind full of the day's events, jack once again tossed and tossed until the early hours, but he couldn't get to sleep.

Come on, boy. We've got to get to the bottom of this mystery...

...and I think we should start with that sinister grocer

Woof!

Jack and Silver dressed quickly and hurried down the darkened Northumbrian lanes into Embleton...

They hid by the grocers shop and watched, and waited for what seemed like hours, until...

Look, Silver ...a lorry!

And there's Mr. Redpath...

...he's signalling to the driver.

McTAVISH SHORTBREAD of SCOTLAND

REDPATH GROCERS

Careful, boy. Don't let them see you.

REDPATH

Och!

Hoots!

Crivens!

So that's his game...

...old Redpath is smuggling illegal Scotsmen across the border in tins of shortbread...

...they're stealing our trousers, taking them back to Scotland and no doubt selling them on the black market. I'm sure they'd fetch a pretty penny in the land of the kilt.

HONK!

Silver crept forward for a better look, but...

It's a dog!... And he's seen everything!

Grab him, quick!

7

As the evil Redpath grabbed hold of the dog detective, Jack ran for help...

...and it wasn't long before a breathless Jack arrived at Embleton Police House...

...where he woke PC Brown...

Puff! Pant! Puff! Pant! Puff! Pant!

What is it boy?... ...are you trying to tell me something?

Why...I do believe you want me to follow you

Puff! Pant!

Hang on, Jack... I'll get my coat

As they ran back, Jack told PC Brown all about Mr Redpath's dastardly plot...

Meanwhile, in the backroom of Mr. Redpath's shop...

Heh! Heh! Another braw nicht's trooser theft. These beauties'll hae a street value o' muckle bawbees back in Glasgae

Och aye! Yon slacks're worth up tae twa poond a pair.

Come on, hurry up! Your bus back to Scotland leaves at dawn.

Suddenly...

Hold it right there, Redpath! The game's up!

Crivens!

Whit the hoots!?

Jings!

Help m'boab!

That's what you think, PC Brown...one step closer and the dog gets it.

I think he means it!

But the village bobby was not to be outdone so easily. With lightning agility, he reached into his pocket for his regulation Northumbrian Constabulary ninja death stars and threw them with deadly accuracy.

THUK! THUK! THUK!

WOOOOAAAAAA-WAH!

Then he finished the job with his samurai sword...

THWIT!

HIAAA-OOOO-WAAAAH!

Wow!! That was super, PC Brown. How exciting!

Thanks, Jack san. Just doing my job.

Later that afternoon...

I just popped round to say well done, Jack. Thanks to you, one of England's worst Scotsman smuggling rings has been broken.

What happened to all the illegal Scotsmen?

You've no need to worry about them, Meg. Our dog handling team chased them into the river Tweed. They were drowned.

Did you here that, Silver? They were all drowned, every man Jock of them

And as a reward, Jack... a pair of long trousers recovered from the shop.

I'm afraid Jack won't be needing those after all, PC Brown.

Eh!?!

You see, those weren't pubes I spotted under my bridge the other night...Silver was moulting, and he was in the bath with me. They were just a few of his stray hairs which clung to me as I stood up

But I'll keep these for when his balls do drop.

Still, you know what they say, PC Brown......pubic hair today, gone tomorrow!

Ha! Ha! Ha!

Ha! Ha! Ha!

The End

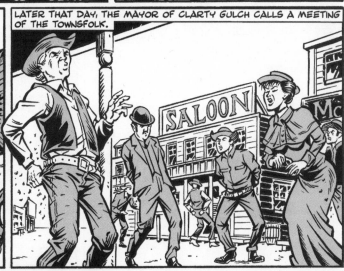

"BRING 'EM BACK" O'LIVE!

O'LIVE WAS DEEP IN THE JUNGLE OF THE AMAZON RAINFOREST WITH HIS ASSISTANT SABU, COLLECTING WILD BEASTS FOR THE WORLD FAMOUS NEW YORK ZOO.

SHHH! I THINK I CAN HEAR HIM NOW.

THERE HE IS, SABU. WHAT A BRUTE!

HIM SEVEN FOOT AT LEAST. MUCH DANGER DANGER, BOSS.

YES, BUT YOU KNOW WHAT THEY SAY, 'THE BIGGER THEY ARE, THE HARDER THEY FALL!'

WITHOUT WASTING A SECOND, O'LIVE LEAPT INTO THE CLEARING AND SQUARED UP TO HIS URSINE ADVERSARY.

RAAAARGH!!!

MICK "BRING 'EM BACK" O'LIVE WAS THE WORLD'S MOST FAMOUS ANIMAL TRAPPER THANKS TO THE UNUSUAL METHODS HE USED. FOR INSTEAD OF NETS, TRAPS AND TRANQUILIZER DARTS, THE FORMER BARE KNUCKLE CHAMPION CAPTURED HIS WILD QUARRY USING HIS FISTS!

RAAAARGH!!!

YOU'LL HAVE TO BE FASTER THAN THAT, YOU OVER-GROWN HEARTH RUG. NOW IT'S MY TURN!

GROOF!!!

DUFF!

DUFF!

A QUICK ONE-TWO, WINNIE THE POOH!..

...AND THEN IT'S OFF TO BED, TED.

GROOOARGH!!!

SOCK!!!

YOU GOT HIM GOOD, BOSS. HIM NOT KNOW WHAT HIT HIM.

YES. I'VE JUST A FEW MORE CRITTERS TO ROUND UP AND THEN IT'S BACK TO CAMP, SABU.

GROAN!!!

O'LIVE WASTED NO TIME...

CRACK!!

THWACK!!!

SLAM!!

SHORTLY.

...3 RHINOCEROSES...A BRACE OF GIRAFFE...2 CROCODILES...HALF A DOZEN OKAPI AND 3 LEOPARDS. YES, I THINK THAT'S THE LOT, SABU.

TIME TO GET THIS LOT BACK TO NEW YORK.

CROCODILES X 2

SUDDENLY.

MR O'LIVE! MR O'LIVE! A JUNGLE TELEGRAM FOR YOU, MR O'LIVE!

WHAT THE...?

TELEGRAM UNION BROOKLYN

+++FROM DIRECTOR NY ZOO+++

+++TO O'LIVE AMAZON RAINFOREST+++

HEARD STORY OF GIANT APE TONKU

ON UNCHARTED ISLAND

52° 32' N 2° 5' W STOP

PLEASE INVESTIGATE STOP

IF TRUE BRING BACK ALIVE STOP

THE GIANT APE, EH? WELL, THERE'S NO MONKEY ON EARTH CAN GO THREE ROUNDS WITH MICK O'LIVE, EH, SABU!

HO-HO! TOO RIGHT, BOSS. YOU MUCH FIGHTY FIGHTY.

THE NEXT DAY, O'LIVE AND HIS FAITHFUL BEARER SET SAIL FOR THE TROPICAL ARCHIPELAGO THAT WAS REPUTED TO BE TONKU'S LAIR...

THIS ISLAND HAS MUCH BAD JUJU, BOSS.

KEEP YOUR OLD-FASHIONED SUPERSTITIONS TO YOURSELF, SABU. WE'VE GOT A GIANT MONKEY TO CATCH.

O'LIVE AND HIS TRUSTY BORDER-LINE-RACIST-STEREOTYPE SIDEKICK HACKED THROUGH THE DENSE UNDER-GROWTH, LOOKING FOR EVIDENCE OF THEIR GARGANTUAN SIMIAN QUARRY.

THEN...

GREAT SCOTT! IT'S A RUINED AZTEC TEMPLE OF THE INCAS!

YES, BOSS. THIS IS STATUE OF ARUCARIA. HIM HEAP ANGRY GOD.

13

SUDDENLY... WHAT THE DEUCE...?

WAAA!!

LOOK AT THE SIZE OF THIS BANANA SKIN! TONKU MUST BE VERY CLOSE.

B...B...BOSS! LOOK! HE NOT JUST CLOSE...HE VERY VERY CLOSE!

GNNNN!

QUICK, SABU! I THINK HE'S GOING TO THROW ONE OF HIS TURDS AT US!

RUN FOR IT!

YES, BOSS!

BLIMBO BLAMBO!

GRAAARGH!!

SPLATCH!

LATER, SAFELY BACK ON THE BEACH, O'LIVE WEIGHED UP HIS OPTIONS.

WE GO BACK, BOSS. HIM HEAP TOO BIG, EVEN FOR YOU.

NO, SABU. I'VE NEVER TURNED MY BACK ON A FIGHT IN MY LIFE.

YOU MAD, MICK O'LIVE! TO LAMP TONKU, YOU NEED FIST AS BIG AS GREAT GOD ARUCARIA!

HEH-HEH!

I THINK YOU'VE JUST GIVEN ME AN IDEA!

SHORTLY.

PUFF! I STILL NOT UNDERSTAND WHY YOU WANT HAND OF STATUE, BOSS. PUFF! PANT!

YOU'LL SEE, SABU. IT'S ALMOST FINISHED.

SAW! SAW!

15

NEXT WEEK! MICK O'LIVE AND SABU TRAVEL TO JAPAN TO CATCH A FIRE-BREATHING GODZILLA FOR FLAMINGOLAND IN KIRBY MISPERTON, NORTH YORKSHIRE.

STONE MASON

THE GRANITE CENTRE FORWARD OF BARNCHESTER ROVERS

TOMMY MASON WAS THE BEST CENTRE FORWARD BARNCHESTER HAD EVER SEEN UNTIL HE FELL VICTIM TO A CURSE, AFTER CHEEKING A FAIRGROUND GYPSY. TURNED TO SOLID GRANITE, IT LOOKED LIKE HIS CAREER WAS OVER. BUT BRAVELY HE FOUGHT BACK FROM HIS MISFORTUNE...

...AND EVENTUALLY REGAINED HIS PLACE IN THE ROVERS FRONT LINE.

AFTER A HARD TRAINING SESSION, THE BARNCHESTER PLAYERS WERE GOING HOME FOR A WELL-EARNED REST BEFORE THE FOLLOWING DAY'S FA CUP FINAL.

SIGN THIS PLEASE, MISTER.

ALRIGHT, SONNY, BUT THEN IT'S HOME FOR SOME KIP BEFORE OUR TRIP TO WEMBLEY.

YOU WANT US TO BEAT LIVERFORD, DON'T YOU?

NOT 'ALF!

COR! LOOK EVERYONE!

WOW! IT'S TOMMY MASON!

WILL YOU SIGN MY PROGRAMME PLEASE, TOMMY?

YOU WERE GREAT AGAINST GRESLEY SPARTANS ON SATURDAY. WHAT A HAT TRICK!

NOW STAND BACK, LADS. LEAVE MR MASON ALONE. MRS MASON'LL HAVE HIS TEA ON THE TABLE, AND WE DON'T WANT IT GETTING COLD, DO WE?

DON'T LET US DOWN.

BRING US BACK THE CUP, TOMMY.

AT HOME.

NOT HUNGRY, LOVE?

YOU MUST BE EXCITED ABOUT THE MATCH, EH?

I'M NOT SUPRISED. TOMORROW IS THE MOST IMPORTANT MATCH OF YOUR CAREER.

I CAN'T WAIT TO TAKE MY PLACE IN THE STANDS AND CHEER YOU ON.

WHY DON'T YOU GET AN EARLY NIGHT?

THE COACH TO WEMBLEY LEAVES FIRST THING TOMORROW. YOU DON'T WANT TO BE LATE.

THE NEXT MORNING, THE SQUAD WERE IN GOOD SPIRITS AS THEY SPED THEIR WAY TO LONDON.

WE'RE GOING TO WIN THE CUP, WE'RE GOING TO WIN THE CUP, E...I...ADDIO, WE'RE GOING TO WIN THE CUP!

BARNCHESTER FA CUP TEAM

THREE O'CLOCK AND THE MATCH KICKED OFF.

PHEEP!

AND HIGH IN THE STANDS BEHIND THE GOAL, ONE VOICE WAS SHOUTING LOUDER THAN THE REST.

COME ON, TOMMY!

UP THE ROVERS

RIGHT FROM THE WHISTLE, BARNCHESTER TOOK THE GAME TO LIVERFORD. TIME AND AGAIN MASON'S SHOTS TESTED THE KEEPER, FORCING HIM TO MAKE SAVE...

OOH, MASON'S HIT THAT LIKE A BULLET!

GOOD SAVE!

...AFTER SAVE...

WHAT A DAISYCUTTER!

YES BUT THE GOALIE MANAGED TO GET A FINGER TO IT.

...AFTER SAVE.

A PILE DRIVER SHOT!

YES, MASON'S GOT HIS SHOOTING BOOTS ON TODAY.

THERE'S THE HALF-TIME WHISTLE. IT'S NIL NIL.

PHEEP!

I CAN'T SEE THE LIVERFORD KEEPER SOAKING UP MASON'S PRESSURE FOR ANOTHER 45 MINUTES.

IT'S ONLY A MATTER OF TIME BEFORE TOMMY STARTS TO FIND THE ONION BAG.

WHEN HE GETS ONE, HE GETS A HATFUL.

THIS MATCH IS OURS FOR THE TAKING, LADS. LIVERFORD DON'T KNOW WHAT DAY IT IS.

ALF...STAN, KEEP PASSING IT ABOUT. DON'T GET CAUGHT IN POSSESSION

YES, BOSS.

SID AND BILL. YOU TWO KEEP IT TIGHT IN MIDFIELD. PLAY IT WIDE AND SQUARE. OPEN UP THE GAME.

YOU CAN COUNT ON US, BOSS.

AND TOMMY, DON'T WORRY...

...IT'LL COME.

NOW LET'S GET BACK OUT THERE AND WIN THAT CUP!

I'LL BE BACK IN A MINUTE WITH THE SACK BARROW FOR YOU, TOMMY.

PRIVATE KNOCK BEFORE ENTERING

LEFT ON HIS OWN IN THE DRESSING ROOM, TOMMY 'STONE' MASON SUDDENLY BECAME AWARE OF A SINISTER FIGURE SNEAKING IN THROUGH THE DOOR.

TOMMY MASON. WELL I NEVER.

YOU'RE HAVING A GOOD GAME, TOMMY. THE WAY YOU'RE PLAYING YOU'RE BOUND TO GET YOUR NAME ON THE SCORE SHEET IN THE SECOND HALF....

...WHICH WOULD BE A SHAME.

YOU SEE, I'VE BET FIFTY POUNDS ON A NO SCORE DRAW.

AND I DON'T LIKE LOSING, MR MASON.

SO IF YOU COULD SEE YOUR WAY CLEAR TO MISSING THE GOAL FOR THE NEXT FORTY-FIVE MINUTES,

...I'D BE EXTREMELY GRATEFUL...

...AND SO WOULD YOUR WIFE! HA! HA! HA!

AS TOMMY MADE HIS WAY ONTO THE PITCH...

...HIS WORST FEARS WERE REALISED.

UP THE ROVER

P-P-PLEASE...DON'T HURT ME!

17

AS THE SECOND HALF GOT UNDERWAY, MASON SEEMED TO HAVE SUFFERED A REMARKABLE DROP IN FORM.

HE'S MISSED THAT ONE.

THAT WAS A SHOT AND IT'S GONE FOR A THROW IN!

WHAT A FARCE!

BOO!

WHAT'S HE THINKING OF? THAT WAS AN OPEN GOAL!

AS THE FINAL WHISTLE APPROACHED, THE CROWD BEGAN TO GROW RESTLESS.

WHAT A LOAD OF RUBBISH!

MASON IS A WANKER MASON IS A WANKER! LA LA LA LA!

MASON'S NEVER GOING TO BRING THE CUP BACK TO BARNCHESTER.

THE SPECTATOR'S COMMENT STRUCK A CHORD IN THE STONE CENTRE FORWARD'S GRANITE HEART, AS HE RE-CALLED THE YOUNG BOYS' WORDS FROM THE DAY BEFORE.

BRING BACK THE CUP, TOMMY!

DON'T LET US DOWN!

TOMMY KNEW HIS NEXT SHOT WOULD HAVE TO BE THE BEST OF HIS LIFE.

SQUARE BALL. TOMMY'S IN SPACE!

PUNT!

TOMMY'S SHOT WAS TRUE.

ROVERS

GREAT SHOT, TOMMY LOVE.

SPLAMM

AIEEE!

WITH HIS WIFE SAFE, MASON COULD ONCE AGAIN FOCUS ON THE GAME, AND AS THE REFEREE CHECKED HIS WATCH, TOMMY KNEW HE HAD TO ACT FAST.

MASON'S LOST HIS MARKER AND THE KEEPER'S OFF HIS LINE. IF I CAN JUST CHIP HIM AND FIND TOMMY ON THE EDGE OF THE SIX YARD BOX.

GOAL!

PHEEEP!

BARNCHESTER WIN! HOORAY!

TOMMY 'STONE' MASON LIFTED THE FA CUP THAT DAY. HE WENT ON TO PLAY ANOTHER IS SEASONS FOR BARN-CHESTER, WINNING THE FA CUP A FURTHER THREE TIMES AND TAKING HIS TEAM TO FOUR LEAGUE TITLES AND THE PRESTIGIOUS EUFA CHAMPIONSHIP. HE RETIRED FROM FOOTBALL IN 1968.

SUCH WAS HIS CONTRIBUTION TO BOTH THE GAME, AND ROVERS, THAT IN 1989 THE CLUB ERECTED A BRONZE STATUE AT THE ENTRANCE TO THEIR GROUND. HE DIED SHORTLY AFTER IN 1990 BUT TODAY EVERYONE WHO GOES TO SEE THE TEAM IS REMINDED OF THE GLORY YEARS UNDER THE CAPTAINCY OF TOMMY 'STONE' MASON, THE GRANITE CENTRE FORWARD OF BARNCHESTER ROVERS.

THE STORY OF ONE MAN'S STRUGGLE AGAINST THE ELEMENTS...A MAN WHO GAVE...

THE GREATEST GIFT OF ALL

CHRISTMAS EVE, 1912. CAPTAIN ERNEST CHEVIOT AND LIEUTENANTS GEORGE PARKIN AND HARRY FLOWERS OF THE ROYAL GEOGRAPHICAL ANTARCTIC EXPEDITION WERE HALF WAY ACROSS THE ROSS ICE SHELF ON THEIR WAY TO THE MAGNETIC SOUTH POLE.

OKAY CHAPS, THE WEATHER'S STARTING TO GO BELLY UP. HOW ABOUT WE CALL IT A DAY?

SOUNDS A GOOD IDEA TO ME, CAPTAIN.

COUNT ME IN.

WE COULD BE STUCK IN FOR A WHILE AND NOT MAKE THE POLE FOR CHRISTMAS DAY. JUST SEVEN MILES AWAY. SO CLOSE AND YET SO FAR, EH?

YES. ROTTEN LUCK THAT.

CHINS UP, MEN. THE STORM MAY BLOW ITSELF OUT. IF IT DOESN'T WE'LL JUST HAVE TO SPEND BOXING DAY AT THE POLE.

STEP TO IT. UNLESS YOU FANCY SLEEPING AL FRESCO TONIGHT, WHAT?

HA! NO FEAR, CAPTAIN.

WE'LL GET THE TENT PUT UP AND GET INTO THAT OLD CHRISTMAS SPIRIT AS BEST WE CAN, EH?

AS THE BLIZZARD PICKED UP IT'S PACE, THE MEN PITCHED THEIR TENT WITH MILITARY DISCIPLINE AND WELL PRACTICED EASE...

THERE WE GO.

AND NOT BEFORE TIME. IT'S GETTING COLDER THAN A DAY ON BRIGHTON BEACH.

I SAY, FLOWERS, DON'T EXAGGERATE!

SHORTLY...

NOT AS SNUG AS BASE CAMP ONE-TON, BUT SHE'LL DO.

HOW ABOUT WE BREAK OUT THE CHRISTMAS PROVISIONS, MEN... MAKE THIS PLACE A LITTLE MORE FESTIVE?

GOOD IDEA, CAPTAIN.

I'VE GOT THREE CIGARS AND A BOTTLE OF BRANDY. THAT SHOULD WARM US THROUGH.

I SAY, GOOD SHOW, CAPTAIN.

MY OLD GIRL HAS MADE US THIS PLUM PUDDING. AND I'VE GOT THREE CRACKERS TO GO WITH IT.

YOU LAY THE CRACKERS OUT, FLOWERS, AND I'LL GET THE TREE UP...

RIGHTY-HO!

I PACKED A BOX OF GLASS BAUBLES TOO, ONLY I'M AFRAID A FEW OF THEM BOUGHT IT WHEN I TOOK A TUMBLE DOWN THAT CREVASSE.

NOT TO WORRY, PARKIN. THERE'S STILL ENOUGH TO MAKE A GOOD SHOW.

NOW THE BUTCHER RECKONED ON 20 MINUTES PER POUND...

...THOUGH HEAVEN KNOWS HOW WE THAW THE BLIGHTER OUT?

WHEN I WAS ON SCOTT'S LITTLE JAUNT A COUPLE OF CHRISTMASSES AGO WE HAD A GOOSE, AND WE THAWED THAT OUT BY STICKING IT IN A SLEEPING BAG.

DO YOU FANCY ROAST, MASH OR BOTH, CHAPS?

BOTH WOULD BE TICKETY-BOO.

I'LL GET THE SPROUTS ON.

THREE HOURS LATER...

GOO-OOOD TI-DINGS OF CO-OM-FORT AND JOY, COMFORT AND JOY, GOO-OOD TI-I-DINGS OF CO-OM-FORT AND JOY.

WHAT A SPLENDID MEAL. CAN'T THINK WHEN I'VE HAD BETTER. AND THANK YOU FOR THE SLIPPERS, FLOWERS. JUST MY SIZE. AND FOR THE PIPE, PARKIN. MOST THOUGHTFUL.

OH, DON'T MENTION IT. I DIDN'T KNOW WHAT TO GET YOU.

A TOAST TO THE KING.

9.20PM. I AM BEING ATTACKED BY A POLAR BEAR. THE BRUTE HAS BITTEN ONE OF MY ARMS OFF, BUT I MUST PRESS ON. I HAVE LET MY FRIENDS DOWN. I SHALL GET THOSE NUTCRACKERS OR DIE TRYING.

10PM. I HAVE AT LAST REACHED CAMP ONE-TON. THERE IS FOOD AND WARMTH HERE. I AM SO TIRED BUT I CANNOT REST. DAMN THESE NUTCRACKERS.

12.20AM. I AM ON WAY BACK TO THE TENT. WITH EVERY STEP I CURSE MY FORGETFULNESS. THE BLIZZARD IS SO STRONG I CAN BARELY SEE MY REMAINING HAND IN FRONT OF MY FACE.

1.45AM. I AM BEING ATTACKED BY A POLAR BEAR AGAIN. I HAVE LOST MY LEFT LEG AND RIGHT BUTTOCK. DAMN THESE BEASTS.

2.15 AM. ONLY TWO MILES TO GO. I AM SO WEAK. I HAVE LOST THE TOES OF MY REMAINING LEG AND GONE COMPLETELY SNOW BLIND. GOD HELP ME.

3.45AM. THE TENT IS NOW IN SIGHT. BUT I AM SO WEARY. GOD HELP ME TO MAKE THE LAST HALF MILE.

SHORTLY...

WELL, IT'S OVER 12 HOURS SINCE HE WENT OUT, CAPTAIN.

YES. I THINK WE'VE GOT TO FACE IT, PARKIN. HE'S NOT COMING BACK.

HE WAS A BLOODY FOOL TO SET OUT THERE IN HIS VEST AND PANTS IF YOU ASK ME...

...BUT HE WAS THE BRAVEST FOOL I EVER MET.

HERE, HERE.

AH WELL! WE'LL OPEN THE TERRY'S CHOCOLATE ORANGE INSTEAD, EH? WE CAN 'TAP IT AND UNWRAP IT' IN HIS MEMORY.

IT'S OUTSIDE ON THE SLEDGE, CAPTAIN. I'LL GO AND GET IT.

OH MY GOD!!

WHAT IS IT, OLD BOY?

WELL, IT LOOKS LIKE HE MADE IT AFTER ALL.

YES. AND LOOK, THERE'S HIS JOURNAL.

FLOWERS LAST ENTRY MADE FOR GRIM READING...

HAVE REACHED THE TENT. I CAN HEAR THE OTHERS INSIDE, BUT I AM TOO WEAK TO CALL OUT. I CAN ONLY TRUST TO THE LORD THAT THEY FIND MY MORTAL REMAINS WITH THE NUTCRACKERS BEFORE THE SNOW COVERS MY BODY. I ASK THAT THE FINDER OF THIS JOURNAL TELL MY BELOVED WIFE FLORENCE AND MY SIX CHILDREN THAT I LOVE THEM, AND THAT THEY WERE IN MY THOUGHTS TO THE VERY END....

THAT LEAVES ONE FEELING A LITTLE HUMBLED, PARKIN.

INDEED IT DOES, CAPTAIN. INDEED IT DOES.

AND SO, AT DAWN...

...A MAN WHOSE HONOUR WAS SURPASSED ONLY BY HIS BRAVERY. HE DID NOT DIE IN VAIN, AND AS WE COMMIT HIS BODY TO THE EARTH...

WE ASK THAT YOU TAKE HIS SOUL INTO YOUR KEEPING. AMEN.

AMEN.

RIGHT. FANCY A NUT, PARKIN?

NOT FOR ME, CAPTAIN, I'M ALLERGIC. BUT YOU HAVE SOME.

HMM! I THINK I'D RATHER HAVE THE TERRY'S CHOCOLATE ORANGE, YOU KNOW.

The End

A DAY IN THE LIFE OF A
FIRE MAN

THE Fire Brigade. Dial 999 and they'll be there in seconds, with sirens wailing and blue lights flashing. Each day they might tackle anything from a chip pan fire in an old folks' home to a raging inferno at a petrochemical refinery. No two shifts in the job are alike, but let's take a look behind the doors of a busy city centre Fire Station and see what happens during a typical day in the front line of the fight against man's deadliest enemy.

07.30 Green Watch are clocking out after a quiet night on duty, but who knows what may lie in store for Blue Watch who are about to begin their 12-hour shift. Because fires can break out at any time, firefighters are no strangers to missed meals, so it is important that they eat whenever they get the chance. That's why the day starts with a good breakfast of sausages, bacon, beans, fried eggs, fried bread and black pudding.

08.00 Breakfast is over, and tension is high as the men of Blue Watch retire to the day room to await the first call of the day. All seems quiet for now, but everyone knows that at any second they could be called away to rescue hundreds of people from a skyscraper which is being consumed by flames. The firefighters relax in many ways; reading books, listening to classical music, playing chess or watching hardcore pornographic videos.

10.38 It's been a quiet shift so far, but everyone is only too aware that all that could change in the blink of an eye. With a second's notice the alarm bell could sound, sending Blue Watch off to put their lives on the line once more, perhaps battling a massive blaze at a gasworks. To ensure that they have the energy to cope with whatever the day may throw at them, they relax with tea and biscuits whilst watching *European Cum Bath Volume 4*.

11.15 The alarm bell rings and it's action stations. Within seconds, the day room is a whirl of activity. The video is paused as the men of Blue Watch prepare to set out on their first job of the day. As they pull on their uniforms and leap aboard the shiny red tender, they have no idea what lies in store. It could be a simple domestic house fire, or it might turn out to be two fully-loaded jumbo jets that have collided mid air over the town centre.

11.23 After tearing through the streets with their siren wailing and lights flashing, the firefighters arrive to find a tearful old lady whose cat is stuck up a tree. At this point, their many hours of training come into play as they go into action like a well-oiled machine. Within seconds the cat is brought safely down and the grateful old lady serves up a well-earned tray of tea and biscuits. She will be sent an invoice for £850 later in the week.

11.58 After the excitement of the morning, the men wind down with a few snacks whilst watching the rest of *European Cum Bath*, followed by *Bukakke Babes* volumes 6 and 7. It is important for them to be mentally and physically relaxed as at any moment they could find themselves back in the engine, speeding towards a plastics plant which is uncontrollably ablaze, belching out a massive plume of thick, black, toxic smoke.

12.32 It is lunchtime, and once again the tender is back on the road, siren screaming. Hitting speeds of 60mph or more it hurtles through the narrow streets, ignoring red lights and stop signs in a desperate bid to get its precious cargo of fish and chips back to the station before they get cold. Keeping the brave firemen of Blue Watch well fed is vitally important as at any moment they could be called away to battle a forest fire threatening to engulf entire villages.

13.20 Firefighters have to keep themselves in peak physical condition since they know that any moment they could be clambering up a 200-foot ladder and carrying an unconscious, fully-grown man down to safety from a towering inferno. That's why, when they are not eating fried food or relaxing in front of *Cum Stained Casting Couch*, the members of Blue Watch keep themselves in tip-top shape playing volleyball, basketball or snooker.

14.09 The alarm rings for the second time that day and once again it's action stations. *Fucktruck Volume 14* is paused as the men of Blue Watch take to the tender. As in any emergency situation time is of the essence, so it is not until they are on the road that they find out what lies in store for them at their destination. It could be a simple bonfire which has got out of control, or it may be a blaze in a furniture warehouse billowing clouds of deadly cyanide gas.

14.19 Happily, there's no need for the breathing apparatus on this occasion, as the emergency turns out to be a young woman who has got her toe stuck in the bathtap. It is a routine job of the sort that firefighters are called out to all the time. But the chief officer knows that things could go wrong, so he decides to call in Yellow and Red Watches from a neighbouring station. With all these firefighters on hand, the woman's rescue is assured.

15.03 With thanks all round the men return to the station to finish watching *Fucktruck Facials 3*. Then it's time for bacon sandwiches all round while they take it easy watching *Cum on My Tiny Tits Volume 4*. It's been a hectic day, but no matter how tired the men of Blue Watch feel, they have to remain alert. They know that at any time they could be called out to a fire on the seventh floor of a 25-storey block of flats with 200 people stuck on the roof.

18.30 Firemen are an essential part of the community, and one of the men of Blue Watch takes an hour off his busy schedule to partake in a little community service. Firefighters regularly give talks about fire prevention to the public, or take their fire engine along to school fetes to press home their safety message. On this occasion he is demonstrating how a fireman takes off his uniform to a group of young women on a hen night.

19.24 All hands are back at the station and everyone is taking a well-earned breather watching *Anal Angels Volume 2*. There may only be a few minutes left of their shift but, like coiled springs, the men of Blue Watch remain constantly on the alert. At any time they could be called out to a motorway pile-up where a water tanker has collided with a lorry carrying enormous lumps of sodium, which has then been hit by a tanker carrying oxyacetylene.

19.30 It's the end of the shift, and for the first time in 12 hours the men of Blue Watch can switch off, both mentally and physically. For one or two, it is straight home to catch up on some long overdue sleep, but for the majority it's straight back to work in the petrol station, driving a mini-cab or stacking shelves at the local supermarket. Meanwhile, for the men of Red Watch the night begins with the first showing of *Two Cocks Up One Cunt*.

Lives of the Saints

This week:

St. Ivel

Patron Saint of Processed Cheese

Nothing captures the taste of summer better than a picnic. Chicken legs, scotch eggs, crisps and ginger beer taste all the better for being eaten in the open air, under a grey sky with the impending threat of drizzle. But have you ever wondered why the cheese sandwiches never taste very nice and always get left half-eaten? To find out you must travel back in time over 700 years.

It all started in 1275 in the hills of Cumberland. Brother Ivel was a monk at the Monastery of Saint Barnabas. It was his duty to tend the small herd of goats kept by the brothers. Every day he took them to the hills where they ate the lush grass, and every evening he milked them and turned their milk into wonderful cheeses. These cheeses were so delicious that his fame spread throughout the olden days.

Now every year, the monks held a picnic for the children who lived in the orphanage of a nearby village. The highlight of this treat was always Brother Ivel's wonderful cheese sandwiches. But at every picnic he saw that the fatter, greedier orphans took more than their fair share of the sandwiches, leaving the thinner, weedier ones with nothing to eat. "Poor child, for it is you who needs my cheese the most" he said.

As he tended his goats that evening, he began to think about how the picnics were being spoilt for many of the orphans. "It seems so unjust" he thought. "If only there was a process that would make my cheese less appealing. That way, the greedy ones would be put off a bit. The other children would then get their fair share of sandwiches, even if they didn't like them very much".

The next day, Brother Ivel set about making his cheese off-putting to eat. After making a block, he cut it up into slices and shoved it down the crack of his arse. He then went out into the fields and began to work up a sweat by digging ditches in the heat of the midsummer sun. However, this made his cheese **too** unpalatable, and not even the weedy orphans would touch it.

Disheartened, the monk went back to tending his goats. As he watched them, he began to wonder. "These lowly creatures," he thought. "Are they not more simple than I? And yet, has not God bestowed upon them the gift of turning grass into milk?" He knew then, that he must ask God for help in making his cheese more disagreeable.

So it was, that Brother Ivel set off into the wilderness of the Cumberland hills, taking with him only a staff and a shawl to stave off the chill summer nights. There he stayed for forty days and forty nights. All the time he prayed to God to reveal the nature of the process he sought. But he was given no sign, and forsaken, he set off back to the monastery.

He arrived back one morning and was alarmed to find that in his absence, his goats had wandered into a part of the garden where rubber trees grew, and he saw that they had been eating the bark. When he took their milk that evening, he saw it had a strange fluorescent yellow tinge to it. He was about to discard the spoiled milk, but decided instead to turn it into cheese for the birds which fed in the garden.

Keeping a firm rein on his excitement and clutching his cheese, the monk rushed into the courtyard to feed the birds. He threw some crumbs onto the floor and was amazed to see that they bounced like little superballs. The sparrows, who usually gorged themselves voraciously on any offerings, pecked at the cheese timidly. They all quickly lost interest and flew off in search of something else to eat.

And from that day, the monks' annual orphans' picnic was no longer an orgy of greed. A miracle had happened, and everyone took only their fair share of Brother Ivel's cheese sandwiches, and often less. At the end of each picnic, Brother Ivel's heart was lifted when he saw the pile of half-eaten sandwiches that remained.

Brother Ivel died in 1452, but his processed cheese continued to be made by the monks of Saint Barnabas and his ideals lived on. Three centuries later, Pope Benevolent III was served one of Brother Ivel's sandwiches on the annual Vatican picnic. He left most of it, and was so nonplused that he decided to canonise the brother in celebration of his truly bland dairy product.

When the cheese was made, Brother Ivel couldn't help but notice that it had a strange plastic-like feel, and that it had started to sweat, a bit like gelignite. Intrigued, he made a sandwich with the cheese and found that almost immediately, the bread went all soggy, like putty. Never before had one of brother Ivel's sandwiches looked so unappealing.

Brother Ivel fell to his knees. "Thank you, O Lord for your gift of this process" he cried in thankfulness and shame, for in his exile he had doubted the Lord and had felt forsaken. Now he realised that God **had** told him the nature of the process. He had told him exactly how to make his cheese edible but unpleasant. The monk had simply not been listening in the right way.

Brother Ivel knew that he must share with the world this gift from God. Feeding the goats on the rubber trees, he made his new cheese in great quantities, and began to spread it far and wide. And he was delighted to discover that not only was it a bit unpleasant to taste, but it lasted longer than his other cheeses, because not even germs particularly wanted to eat it.

Fragments of St. Ivel's first sandwich remain in a reliquary in the crypt of the church of St. Eden in the Vale. Each year on St. Ivel's birthday, a ceremony, 'The Picnic of St. Ivel', is held in the church. It culminates in the bishop of the diocese being offered the fragments of sandwich, whereupon he ceremoniously lifts the corner of the bread, turns his nose up, and has a Kit-Kat.

LATER.

THIS IS THE CLEARING WHERE MOUNTIE BROWN SAW THE BEAR, JACK.

SUDDENLY, SILVER'S KEEN CANINE SENSE OF SMELL DETECTED SOMETHING.

WHAT IS IT, BOY? WHAT HAS YOUR KEEN CANINE SENSE OF SMELL DETECTED?

SNIFF! SNIFF! SNIFF!

IT'S OKAY. IT'S ONLY A WEAK AND HUNGRY BABY MOOSE...

JACK! LOOK!

ROOOAAARRRR.

QUICK, AUNT MEG! IT'S THE BEAR! SHOOT IT!

WOOF! WOOF!

OKAY, GET BACK!

WHAT'S HAPPENING? WHY ISN'T IT DEAD?

I DON'T KNOW. THE BULLETS ARE JUST BOUNCING OFF IT...

...THERE'S NOTHING I CAN DO!

BANG! BANG! BANG! BANG!

ROOOAAARR!!

ROOOAAARRRR!!!

AAARRGHH!!

SUDDENLY.

I... THINK IT'S GOING. SOMETHING MUST HAVE SPOOKED IT.

YES. LOOKS LIKE WE'LL LIVE TO TELL THE TALE AFTER ALL.

I CAN SAFELY SAY THAT WAS THE MOST TERRIFYING ENCOUNTER WITH A WILD ANIMAL I'VE EVER HAD. JUST LIKE MOUNTIE BROWN, I'VE SHITTED MY PANTS.

ME TOO.

COME ON. IT'S A LONG DUCK WALK TO TOWN FOR US.

WHIMPER!

AN HOUR LATER.

HERE WE ARE, JACK. AND NOT BEFORE TIME. MY MUD FLAPS ARE CHAFFING LIKE NOBODY'S BUSINESS.

MINE TOO!

SALOON

GRANDMA BROWN'S LAUNDERETTE

GENERAL STORE

WOW! IT LOOKS BUSY IN HERE, AUNT MEG.

YES, DOESN'T IT!

SERVICE WASHES $5 $10

OUT OF ORDER

OUT OF ORDER

27

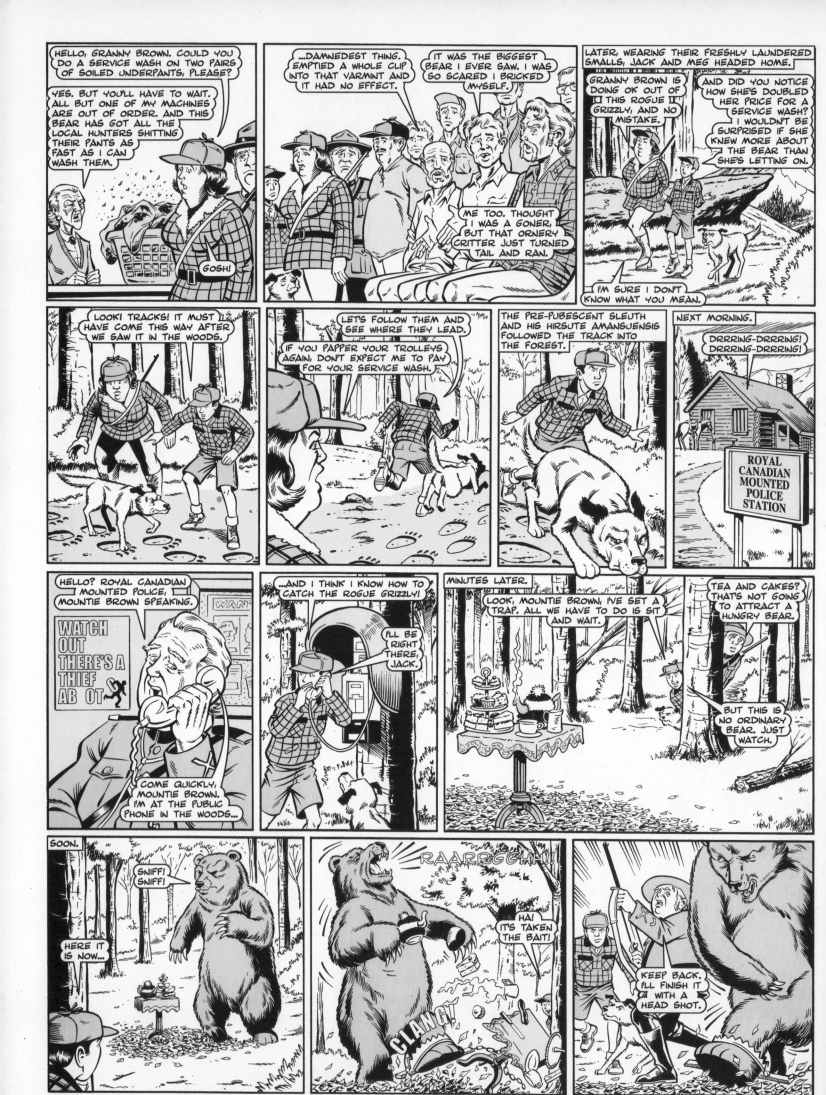

THE END

The End

THE GENERAL ELECTION has once again brought the Houses of Parliament into the public eye. As the new MPs take their place on the government and opposition benches in the Commons, it's time to take a closer look at the inner workings of the world's oldest legislature. For over 600 years the same traditions and rituals have been acted out within the august walls of the Palace of Westminster. Even though the faces of the participants may change with the passing of the years, the characters and roles that they play in the democratic process have remained unchanged for centuries. So who are these people who run the country, and what exactly do they do? Let's see...

1 The Prime Minister
The Prime Minister is the most important person in parliament. He is the leader of the party with the highest number of votes and it is his job to think up all the new laws. But with such great power comes equally great responsibility. When things go wrong, he has to choose a scapegoat who will take the blame and resign to spend more time with his family.

2 The Speaker
Ironically, despite being called the speaker, the speaker is only allowed to say one word: 'Order'. The good news is, he's allowed to say it twice, or in extreme cases three times, in order to stop the MPs misbehaving. Unlike all other politicians, the lucky speaker actually gets to 'live over the shop' in a plush apartment under Big Ben. However the job does have its downside. He must attend every debate from beginning to end whilst dressed as a pantomime pirate!

3 Leader of the Opposition
As the leader of the party with the second highest number of votes, it is the job of the Leader of the Opposition to say the opposite of everything the Prime Minister says. During a Commons exchange, he must make several toe-curlingly lame jokes which will be met with gales of hysterical thigh-slapping laughter from his own MPs.

4 Protestor
A *Fathers for Justice* campaigner dressed as Superman.

5 Jobbing Backbencher
This MP has been representing the same safe seat for decades, yet has never asked a question or spoken in a debate. When his party realises he's still there, he will be swiftly elevated to the house of Lords and his constituency handed on a plate to a young economics graduate who is having a homosexual affair with a cabinet minister.

6 The Malcontent Former High-Flyer
This backbencher is a former political heavyweight who, in a moment of suicidal honesty, actually told the Prime Minister what he thought rather than what he thought the Prime Minister wanted to hear. He has paid for this brief lapse of unintegrity with his parliamentary career.

7 Protestor
A *Fathers for Justice* campaigner dressed as Batman.

8 Back row MPs
The happier a politician is to toe the party line, the closer to the front bench he sits. Consequently, like schoolboys on a bus, the MPs who sit right at the back are the real naughty troublemakers of the party. Back row MPs are more likely to be caught spitting on the other MPs' backs, swapping Yu-Gi-O cards and looking at nudie books than tabling ammendments to white papers, voting in parliamentary divisions or making impassioned speeches on behalf of their constiuents.

9 Black Rod
The age-old post of Black Rod goes back hundreds of years. During the State Opening of Parliament each morning he must approach the door of the chamber in his finery, only to have it slammed in his face by the Queen. Then, in a tradition as old as time, Black Rod must knock three times on the ceiling and twice on the pipe before the door is opened and parliamentary business can commence.

10 Leader of the Third Party
This is perhaps the most enviable position in parliament, for thanks to his complete lack of power or influence the leader of the third party has no responsibilities whatsoever. It is his duty to make the most fabulous and outlandish promises, safe in the knowledge that he runs no risk of ever being called upon to put them into practice.

11 Protestor
A *Fathers for Justice* campaigner dressed as a Dalek.

12 The Celebrity MP
In a tradition dating back to the days of Gladstone, Disraeli and Oliver Cromwell, each parliament must contain at least one former stage or screen celebrity. Although politically competent, such MPs are never be allowed to rise to cabinet level because there's a Ken Russell film which turns up regularly on BBC2 where you can see their moth-eaten twat.

13 The Front Bench
The Front Benches are where ministers, secretaries of state, members of the cabinet and members of the shadow cabinet sit. A Front Bencher's job is to crush up to the middle so that their toadying face is in shot when their party leader watches himself on telly later that day to see who's been agreeing with him the best.

14 Protestor
The son of a has-been pop singer campaigning for the Countryside Alliance.

15 Whips
In olden times it was the Whips' job to get drunken members of parliament out of the local taverns and brothels so that they could take part in important votes. However, times have changed and nowadays the Whips concern themselves with getting drunken members out of the local bars and lapdancing clubs so they can take part in important votes.

16 Press Gallery
It is the parliamentary correspondent's job to listen carefully to every debate before using his skill and knowledge to distil the most important points for his readership. Either that, or he just waits for John Prescott to open his mouth and writes down what he says word for word in a humorous 'parliamentary sketch' column before heading for the bar.

17 Parliamentary Guards
Security is paramount in the Lower Chamber. The security staff at the House of Commons make an intimidating sight in their frock coats, ruffles, velvet breeches, ladies' tights and 'pantomime principal boy' shoes. Any intruder bent on throwing coloured flour at the Prime Minister's back would have to easily get past this ornamental squad of bewildered octogenarians first.

Next Week: Who's Who at Guantanamo Bay

"SPITFIRE" McGUIRE
& his home-made mini-plane in
JERRY TAKES A PASTING

It's 1945 – and once again the hun are being given what-for by the brave fly-boys of England's RAF. Flying each night from their Lincolnshire airfields deep into the black heart of Germany's Rhineland to deliver their deadly payloads of high explosive, these giants of the sky return each morning riddled with bullet holes and torn by Nazi flack.

At the controls of his Lancaster bomber, Wing Commander Tommy "Spitfire" McGuire released his last bomb and headed back for blighty.

SORRY JERRY, THAT'S ALL FOR TONIGHT. I'M OFF HOME FOR SOME BACON AND EGGS.

BANDITS AT THREE O'CLOCK SKIP!

WE'RE SITTING DUCKS IN THIS LUMBERING OLD CRATE.

AAGH! I'M HIT!

GINGER'S BOUGHT IT.

Bosch air ace Hauptmann Klaus Von Umlaut congratulated himself on yet another kill.

HA! HA! THAT BRINGS MY TOTAL TO FORTY-TWO. I AM THE GREATEST FIGHTING ACE THE LUFTWAFFE HAS EVER SEEN!

But the game was not yet lost. Displaying English bulldog grit, McGuire set to work assembling his home-made mini-plane from the kit of parts he kept in his parachute back-pack.

Within seconds the prefabricated craft was assembled and the engine was running.

With inches to spare, McGuire pulled out of his dive...

CRUMBS! THAT WAS A NARROW SQUEAK! ANOTHER COAT OF PAINT AND I'D HAVE BEEN A GONER!

NOW – I'VE GOT A SCORE TO SETTLE WITH THAT SAUSAGE-EATING SQUAREHEAD.

Expertly, McGuire flew his midget craft under the belly of Von Umlaut's fighter...

HEH HEH! HE'LL NEVER SEE ME HERE.

JERRY'S IN FOR AN UNSCHEDULED LANDING!

HAPPY LANDINGS FRITZ!

DONNERWETTER! MY FUEL TANK IS EMPTY!

34

Without fuel, the German's ME109 stood no chance, and plummeted back towards the airfield.

AIEEE! I AM GOING TO CRASH!

HIMMEL!

AAGH!

Within seconds, the nazi was on his way to hospital.

THINK I'LL KEEP TABS ON THAT KRAUT BONE-WAGON.

Minutes later, the hospital guard was surprised as McGuire flashed out of nowhere towards the main doors, still at the controls of his micro-plane.

IT'S VISITING TIME!

ACHTUNG!

der HOSPITALEN

TAKE ONE OF THESE THREE TIMES A DAY AFTER MEALS HERR DOCTOR!

GEZHUNDHEIT!

AGH!

In Von Umlaut's ward...

SPITFIRE MCGUIRE? BUT IT CAN'T BE!!?!

TIME FOR SOME ENGLISH MEDICINE, UMLAUT!

McGuire's bullet found its mark...

TAKE THAT!

AGH!

SORRY I DIDN'T BRING ANY GRAPES, CHAPS – BUT HERE'S A PRESENT FROM OLD BLIGHTY.

TYPICAL JERRY BUILDERS – FORGOT TO PUT A DOOR IN!

LEIBRAUMILCH!

The hospital exploded, killing all the Germans.

AGH!

AAGH!

HO! HO! NOW TO GET BACK FOR MY BACON AND EGGS – AT LAST!

With Von Umlaut dead, the Luftwaffe's opposition crumbled, leaving England's bombers unopposed as they dropped their deadly cargoes into Germanys cold steel heart, and we won the war.

THE END

HRH Her Royal Highness Queen Elizabeth The Queen Mother
Her Marvellous Life in Pictures

Even now, weeks after her funeral, it's hard to believe the Queen Mother really has gone. Over the 101 years of her long and marvellous life she became as much a part of the British landscape as London buses, bobbies on bicycles two by two, Westminster Abbey, the tower of Big Ben or the rosy red cheeks of the little children.

But now is not a time to allow our overwhelming feelings of sadness and despair to sweep over us. Instead of weeping inconsolably and commiting suicide in order to be with her again, we should try to smile through our tears and celebrate her marvellous life. A life which shone like a marvellous beacon of marvellousness amidst a world full of whatever the opposite of marvellousness is.

1900 From the day she was born, the infant Queen Mother showed signs of being more royal than the other babies in the hospital. She quickly mastered the art of having everything done for her, and by the age of 11 months she was able to wave at people out of her pram and choke on food. These were skills she was to call on every day of her life for the next hundred marvellous years.

1912 In April, the 12 year old queen Mother set sail for America aboard the ill-fated RMS Titanic along with 2340 other souls. The ship hit an icecube in the Atlantic and began to sink. With great presence of mind, she commandeered 3 lifeboats, one for herself, one for her ladies in waiting, and one for her luggage. Selflessly, she steered her boat amongst the hundreds of drowning passengers, lifting their spirits by waving and politely enquiring how long they had been in the water.

1917 With the dark cloud of war hanging over Europe, The people of Britain are encouraged to make do and mend. In June, the King took announced that food rationing was being considered and that everyone must tighten their belts. Showing her mischievous sense of humour, the Queen Mother immediately ordered 5000 slightly smaller belts from the haute couture houses of Paris. The belts, made of everything from leather to panda skin, and encrusted with diamonds and rubies, duly arrived, along with a bill for over 1 million guineas to the British taxpayer. The Queen Mother's delightful joke had cost a mere shilling from every man, woman and child in Britain.

1928 As patron of St. Mary's Hospital, London, the Queen Mother was invited to take tea in the laboratories of Alexander Fleming, at the time a young professor struggling to invent antibiotics. During the visit, she was offered a swan sandwich on which a small amount of crust had inadvertantly been left. Horrified at the crust, she left the sandwich on the bench, where Fleming discovered it three weeks later with all penicillin fungus growing out of it. He later named the strain of mould in honour of the woman whose refined taste had made it possible, Penicillium queenmumensis.

1931 During a State Safari in Rhodesia, The Queen Mother and her husband George VI between them bagged more than 200 Zulus in a single day's shooting. In today's climate, shooting black men for sport may be frowned upon by the politically correct lobby. But in those days it was a perfectly innocent pastime. Indeed, as there are many more black men nowadays than there were in the thirties, it could be argued that the Queen Mum was actually an early conservationist.

1933 Europe in the early thirties was a place of rising social tensions. With war once again brewing on the horizon, the world could seem a frightening place to live. But throughout it all the Queen Mother never once lost her marvellously impish sense of humour. She was often known to sneak out of Buckingham Palace in the early hours and make her way to Jewish districts of London where she mischievously put half bricks through windows and daubed cheeky swastikas on brickwork.

1940 Queues formed in high streets as people lined up for their meagre weekly rations of powdered egg, bacon and sugar. Displaying solidarity with her people, the Queen Mum queued up too, ration book in hand. After standing outside the butchers for nearly eight minutes, she recalled parliament and told them she feared the country would become demoralised if they thought the royal family didn't have enough meat. A bill was forced through, and the Windsors spent the rest of the war on a stone of sausages each every day!

1945 The Queen Mother's unpleasant experiences of having to meet a few working class people during the war had taken their toll, and doctors advised that for her own health she should take it exceptionally easy for a while. Retiring to a darkened room in Balmoral Castle, she placed her forearm across her brow and swooned onto a chaise longue, where she remained completely motionless for 21 years. In 1966 she emerged, declaring herself "greatly refreshed" by her rest. Amazed onlookers could only shake their heads in admiration as she got immediately back to work, sitting in a gold coach waving at people!

1951 During the post war period of reconstruction, the Royal Family decided that they should bring their image more up to date, as it was feared that they could seem out of touch with the ordinary people of Britain. In a monumental lapse of judgement, the King sent nude photos of the Queen Mother to the Readers' Wives section of Fiesta magazine. The pictures, tame by today's standards, showed the Queen Mother posing on the formica top in the kitchen of Buckingham Palace. Half a million copies of the magazine had rolled off the presses before Palace officials got wind of the King's actions. A constituional crisis was narrowly averted when the entire issue was taken out into the middle of the North Sea and dumped in 10,000 ft of water.

1966 Everyone remembers where they were when England won the World Cup in June of 1966. Especially the Queen Mum! With the score at 3-2, this marvellous lady couldn't contain her excitement any more, dashed from the royal box and ran onto the pitch. BBC commentator Kenneth Wolthamstow spotted her and uttered the words "the Queen Mum is on the pitch, she thinks it's all over." The commentary was later re-recorded on the orders of stuffy palace officials.

1978 The Queen Mother's acts of kindness were legendary, but in 1978 they nearly saved a man's life. During a visit from royal doctor Sir Gladstone Gamble one of her butlers collapsed after swallowing his own tongue. Seeing the poor man choking on the floor, she gave the doctor permission to go and assist him as soon as he had finished shaving her bunions. Unfortunately, due to a particularly tough bunion, it was 25 minutes before the butler could receive medical help and by then he had already been dead for quarter of an hour. But the Queen Mother's attempt to save him didn't go unnoticed, and she awarded herself the Victoria Cross in recognition of her extraordinary act of self-sacrifice.

1985 She was famously loyal to her servants, several of them staying with her for many decades. One of them, affectionately known as 'Backdoor Bobby', joined her household as a boy of 13 and stayed with her for more than 50 years. After knowing him for half a century the Queen Mother came to look upon him almost as a human being, and so it broke her heart when she had to dismiss him after he took her afternoon tea with an insufficiently polished teaspoon on the tray.

2002 At the end of a marvellously long life, filled with marvellousness, Britain's favourite grandmother still hadn't lost her sense of fun. On the day she died, relatives wept tears, not of grief and sorrow, but of hysterical laughter. Called to Clarence House to say goodbye, they were treated to a sidesplitting impression of 'Staines Massive' comedian Ali G, complete with Tommy Gear hat, comedy hand gestures and sexually explicit language.

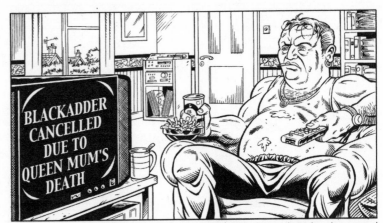

2002 And so, on March 31st our beloved Queen Mother was taken from us before her time. The British people were stunned into going about their daily business as if nothing had happened. But the loss of the most marvellous woman ever to stalk the face of the earth touched people's hearts a thousand times more deeply than the deaths of their own grandmothers ever could. A million times more tragic than ten jumbo jets full of blind orphan toddlers flying into the side of a mountain, the moment of her passing changed the world forever until normal programmes resumed 25 minutes later.

The Shipwrecked Craft Fayre

Shipwrecked in perilous seas and washed ashore on a desert island were the members of the Acorn Craft Fair...

...all members of the ships crew were lost as she went down, save young Tom Bates the cabin boy.

Gasp!

Is everyone alright? Are we all safe?

Right! I don't know where we are and we must assume no one else does. We must eventually devise a means of escape, but until then we'll have to find food, water and make some shelter

Don't worry. We're all craftsfolk. We can all fall back on our various skills and between us we'll survive

Great! It'll be night time soon. I suggest we waste no time and get to work

Let's go

Yeah!

Soon the island became a hive of activity as the craftsfolk pulled together to survive

Shortly...

There! The shelter's done. That'll keep us safe and dry. What's everyone else been doing I wonder?

I've made a lovely rustic nameplate

Ooh! isn't that nice. I love poker work, I do

Eh?

The Elms

I've made some macrame wall hangings

What?...what good are they?

They're nice

Yes. They'll go lovely inside the shelter

She threaded all those beads by hand. Don't say she hasn't pulled her weight!

Look... Did anyone find anything to eat?

Yes, I found bushes covered in all sorts of nuts, fruits and berries. I picked a basketful

Well done. I suggest we ration them out to make them last lon...

No, they're not to eat. I've made them into this traditional rustic harvest display

That's lovely. It'll go well between the macrame hangings.

Look, does anyone have any practical skills which could get us off this island?

Well, I'm a boat builder by trade. I've made us a boat

Great! Let's go and see it

Here it is...

...isn't she a beauty?

Ooh, what detail. It's marvellous

All the rigging and that. How's it done?

Next morning, Tom awoke to find the shelter deserted

At last! They've seen sense and gone out to forage for food and firewood

But...

Oh, no!

ACORN CRAFT FAYRE TODAY ON THE BEACH →

WPC JULIET BRAVO'S SCOTLAND YARD CRIME FILE:

the Covent Garden Diamond Heist

I'M PRETEND WPC JULIET BRAVO. I'VE SOLVED HUNDREDS OF CASES, BUT ONE THING THEY ALL HAVE IN COMMON IS THAT SOMEWHERE ALONG THE LINE, THE CRIMINALS MAKE A MISTAKE. THIS CASE IS NO EXCEPTION...

JANUARY 1978. IN THE BACK ROOM OF A BERMONDSEY PUB, A GROUP OF VILLAINS PLAN A DARING ROBBERY.

SO, GENTS, I THINK YOU ALL KNOW EACH OTHER. SCOTCH FREDDIE IS OUR DRIVER. HE'LL BE WAITING OUTSIDE IN A JAG.

OCH AYE!

BRIAN IS OUR JELLY MAN. HE'S GOING TO GET US THROUGH THE WALL INTO THE SAFE ROOM.

ONCE INSIDE, IT'S UP TO FINGERS HERE. HE'S GOT SEVEN MINUTES TO GET INTO THE SAFE BEFORE THE FILTH ARRIVE.

DO ME A FAVOUR, BOSS. THE SAFE AIN'T BEEN MADE YET WHAT I CAN'T CRACK IN FIVE!

HEH! HEH! NICE ONE, FINGERS.

WATCHING OUR BACK WILL BE BIG RON. YOU BRINGING ANY TOYS ALONG, RON?

YEAH! I'LL HAVE ME SAWN-OFF TO STOP ANY HAVE-A-GO HEROES.

LAST, MAKING SURE WE ALL COME BACK IN ONE PIECE IS MR PERKINS, WHO'S HEALTH AND SAFETY ON THIS TICKLE.

WHAT DO YOU THINK OF THE M.O. SO FAR, MR PERKINS?

NO MAJOR CONCERNS. HOWEVER, WHEN BRIAN JELLIES THE WALL OF THE GAFF, THERE IS NOT AN INCONSIDERABLE RISK OF FALLING MASONRY, SO HARD HATS AND STEEL-TOED RIGGERS MUST BE WORN AT ALL TIMES.

WHAT ABOUT DUST?

I'VE BEEN ONTO THE LOCAL AUTHORITY AND I'VE GOT THE BUILDING REGULATIONS COMPLIANCE CERTIFICATE. I'VE ALSO HAD A TYPE 2 (STANDARD SAMPLING, IDENTIFICATION AND ASSESSMENT) SURVEY DONE TO CHECK FOR HAZARDOUS AND DELETERIOUS MATERIALS AND THE WALL HAS SHOWN UP ASBESTOS FREE SO STANDARD 4 MICRON DUST MASKS WILL BE FINE.

KNOCKOUT!

NEXT DAY.

THE CHARGES ARE ALL SET, BOSS. I'M READY TO BLOW THE WALL.

TAKE COVER, LADS.

AHEM!...

AF DIAMOND ERCHANTS

TO LET

WE HAVE MOVED

WHAT IS IT, MR PERKINS?

BEST GET SOME HAZARD WARNING TAPE UP, JUST IN CASE ANYONE WANDERS BACK INTO THE BLAST ZONE.

I'LL GET ON IT.

JIMMY GELIGNITE SAYS ALWAYS TAKE CARE!

AND COULD SOMEONE MAKE SURE THE POWER HAS BEEN TURNED OFF. THERE COULD BE LIVE WIRES IN THE WALL THAT COULD START A FIRE OR PROVIDE AN ELECTRIC SHOCK HAZARD.

OKAY, MR PERKINS.

A MINUTE LATER.

HONNNNNK!

FIRING IN 30...29 ...28...27...26...

25 SECONDS LATER...

BOOOOM!

DING-A-LING A-LING A-LING-A-LING!

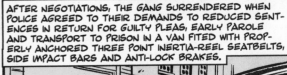

NEXT WEEK: HELD CAPTIVE BY MUTANT SECURITY GUARDS, PROFESSOR PURVES IS TOLD THAT HE NEEDS TO APPLY FOR A PERMIT TO TAKE PHOTOGRAPHS OF THE SUBTERRANEAN ARNDALE CENTRE FOR PUBLICATION PURPOSES. MEANWHILE, IN A BRANCH OF LK BENNETT RUN BY A LOST TRIBE OF CAVE WOMEN, PENELOPE FINDS A DRESS THAT HAS BEEN REDUCED FROM £79.99 TO £19.99.

FROM JUNGLE TO PETE DOHERTY...
THE STORY OF CRACK

EVERYONE loves to see Pete Doherty up to his hilarious, headline-grabbing antics. Whether he's embarrassing himself on stage at Live8 or frantically flushing the toilet every time he hears a police siren, chances are the Babyshambles frontman is ripped to his pale, sweating tits on his favourite drug. But what is it? Where does it come from? And how does it reach Pete? Find out by reading this fascinating tale...

DOHERTY'S crack begins its life 8000 miles across the ocean in Colombia on the mountainous slopes of the Andes where the seeds are sown in the early spring. Suitable areas for cultivation are carefully selected by the growers, and existing food crops such as wheat or corn are cleared to ready the soil for the coca plant.

SIX months later the plants have grown up strong and healthy and are ready for harvesting. The whole family joins in gathering the leaves from the bushes and loading them onto the backs of llamas. These sturdy pack animals are the lorries of the Andes and can carry their own body weight in unprocessed drugs.

BACK at the farm, the coca leaves are trodden in the same way that a French farmer treads grapes to make wine. Once again, all the family join in. The process is well underway, but it will still be many weeks before this green paste is in a form that can get former Libertines singer Pete off his face.

THE farming is over, and now begins a more technical phase. In a secret laboratory hidden deep in the jungle and safe from prying eyes, a scientist has set up a giant chemistry set. He alone understands the magical process whereby the sticky, green paste is refined into the sparkling, white crystals to which Doherty is a hopeless slave.

IT IS time for the rocks of crack to bid farewell to the land of their birth. In an airport hotel room, a man known as a 'mule' collects his precious cargo. The drugs are carefully wrapped in special balloons and packed safely inside him before he begins an exciting aeroplane journey to London.

DURING his 12-hour flight, the mule can sit back, relax and enjoy the view. However, at lunchtime, he must politely refuse the stewardess's tempting offer of a meal. With fifty ping-pong ball sized parcels of Doherty's crack packed in his rectum, he dare not risk a visit to the toilet.

ON arrival, the 'Nothing to Declare' channel must be negotiated. The experienced mule will choose his moment carefully. He knows that he is less likely to be stopped if he follows a pretty lady, whose suitcase containing bras and skimpy knickers acts as an irresistible lure for the red-blooded customs officers.

IN A hotel room on the other side of London, the importer meets with another business contact known as the distributor, to whom he plans to sell the crack. In the drug business as in many others, there is a lot of dishonesty, and the distributor has to be very careful to check that the drugs are of good quality before handing over his hard earned money.

THE DISTRIBUTOR is a canny businessman and knows that he can maximise his profits if the crack is mixed or 'cut' with cheap substances that look similar. Just like your butcher mixes sawdust and phlegm into his sausage meat, a drugs dealer will mix the crack with rock salt, drain cleaner or crumbled up firelighters.

AT last. After a year long 8000-mile journey from the jungles of South America, Doherty finally has his crack. Eagerly, he pops it into his straight-shooter pipe and has himself a few puffs before going on stage. Producing a brief feeling of euphoria as well as hallucinations, paranoid delusions, erratic heartbeats, itching and delusional parasitosis, it weaves its magic on the talented pop star.

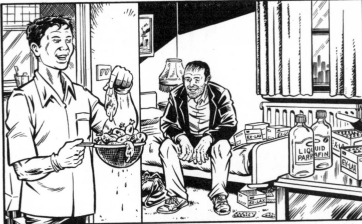

ONCE safely in his hotel, the mule can finally begin unpacking his precious cargo. It is taken off his hands by a London contact, a man known only as the importer. Although it is now in the same city as Pete, there are still several more links in the chain before the drug finds its way into the Babyshambles vocalist's glass crack pipe.

SATISFIED with the quality of the crack, the distributor hands over the cash. The two men shake hands and the drugs deal is done. All that remains now is for the importer to be shot in the back of the head by the distributor's business associates, a process known as whacking, and his money returned.

NOW that the crack has been cut and wrapped into convenient pipe-sized packages, it is finally time for it to hit the streets. A Babyshambles roadie is sent out of the stage door up a back alley to buy Doherty's crack. This is known as 'scoring'. A score of crack will cost Pete's roadie between £10 and £30, depending on how 'dry' the streets are.

THE following day, the world wakes up to the familiar story that Doherty has made a complete arse of himself once more. Meanwhile, on the other side of the world, a field of golden corn is being torched in readiness for the next crop of young coca plants. And so the wonderful crack cycle continues.

Who's Who and What They Do

1 The passenger

Although he funds the entire railway operation, the passenger is the least important person in the station. He is a source of annoyance to all railway staff. Passengers often fail to do their homework and regularly turn up at the ticket booth without knowing the difference between an Off-Peak Silver Saver, an Advance Silver Off-Peak Day Return and an All-Day Off-Peak Silver Return Saver. When he has bought his ticket, chances are the passenger has failed to check in the on-line timetable which platform his train should leave from, and it is left to an overworked platform attendant to shrug his shoulders, mumble something and walk off when faced with his inane questions.

2 Ticket office

The modern ticket office is a state-of-the-art computerised hub of inactivity. Fourteen windows will service the ticket buying needs of the travelling public. A special 'Tickets for Immediate Travel' window serves the needs of those who are in a hurry, and a large queue has built up since it is the only one of the fourteen open.

3 Porters

The porter is the workhorse of the station and it is his job to scuttle away quickly into a Staff Only area when he spots someone who might need help with their luggage. The last British Railways porter who carried a passenger's bag died in 1959.

4 Transport Police

For the comfort and convenience of passengers, there is no smoking allowed within a half mile radius of all UK mainline stations. Here a passenger has been spotted on CCTV flagrantly disregarding this rule, and is being arrested under the Prevention of Terrorism Act by bobbies from the British Transport Police.

5 Platform announcer

It is the job of the platform announcer to keep the passengers in a constant state of confusion. Watching from his booth high above the station, he keeps travellers scurrying back and forth over the bridge by announcing a series of last-minute platform alterations. The ideal person for the platform announcer's job is someone with a clear speaking voice who enunciates his words

THE railway station of today is a fascinating place. Gone are the dusty waiting rooms and wooden fronted ticket offices of yesteryear. The modern railway station is more akin to an airport terminal with its high tech equipment designed to ensure that the trains ave more or less on time. Usually less. Every day, tens of thousands of passengers pass through its concourses. They need to eat, rink, rest and go to the lavatory whilst they wait for their delayed services. All these needs have to be catered for. It is a miracle of ansport logistics and many people are employed to ensure that the whole experience is as unpleasant and expensive as possible. ut who are they, what are their jobs, and why don't they do them properly? Let take a look at *WHO'S WHO IN THE RAILWAY STATION*.

precisely. So the job is given to a stuttering alcoholic who's had a tracheotomy.

6 Refreshments
With trains often running several hours late, the station has a variety of refreshments for a variety of tastes and budgets. So whether you fancy a limp six hour-old burger for £7, or a cup of blistering hot coffee and a piece of shortbread for £7.50, your needs are catered for.

7 Sanitation operative
Hundreds of thousands of people use trains each day, often for very long journeys, so it is important that the on-board lavatories are kept as unusable and unsanitary as possible. Every carriage on every train that pulls into the station is checked by the sanitation operative who ensures that the toilets are clogged up with fresh bangers and mash and that the locks on the door don't function properly.

8 Richard Branson
Spend half a day in any railway station in Britain and you are bound to see Richard Branson. Whether he is dressed as a woman, a bear or a beefeater, he is always to be seen on a publicity photo call promoting his latest service. Then it's off home in a chartered helicopter because he has cancelled his train.

9 Trainspotters
It is a fact that when at a railway station, you are never more than 10 yards from a trainspotter. Like pigeons and rats, they cause a nuisance, getting in the way of commuters and frightening children. With many of them on the sex offenders' register, train companies are trying to discourage their presence by making the carrying of thermos flasks and the eating of salt and vinegar crisps an offence on the platforms.

10 Cleaner
The railway concourse is an enormous public space that sees thousands of people pass through each day. To keep it spick and span requires an army of cleaners, so the railway company employ one man with a mop and bucket of grey water whose job it is to move a 'Caution, Cleaning In Progress' sign around to where it will cause the most inconvenience.

NEXT WEEK • • • •
Who's Who at the Vasectomy Clinic

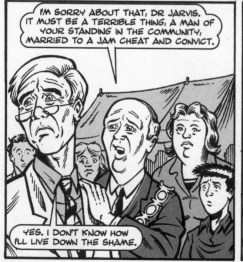

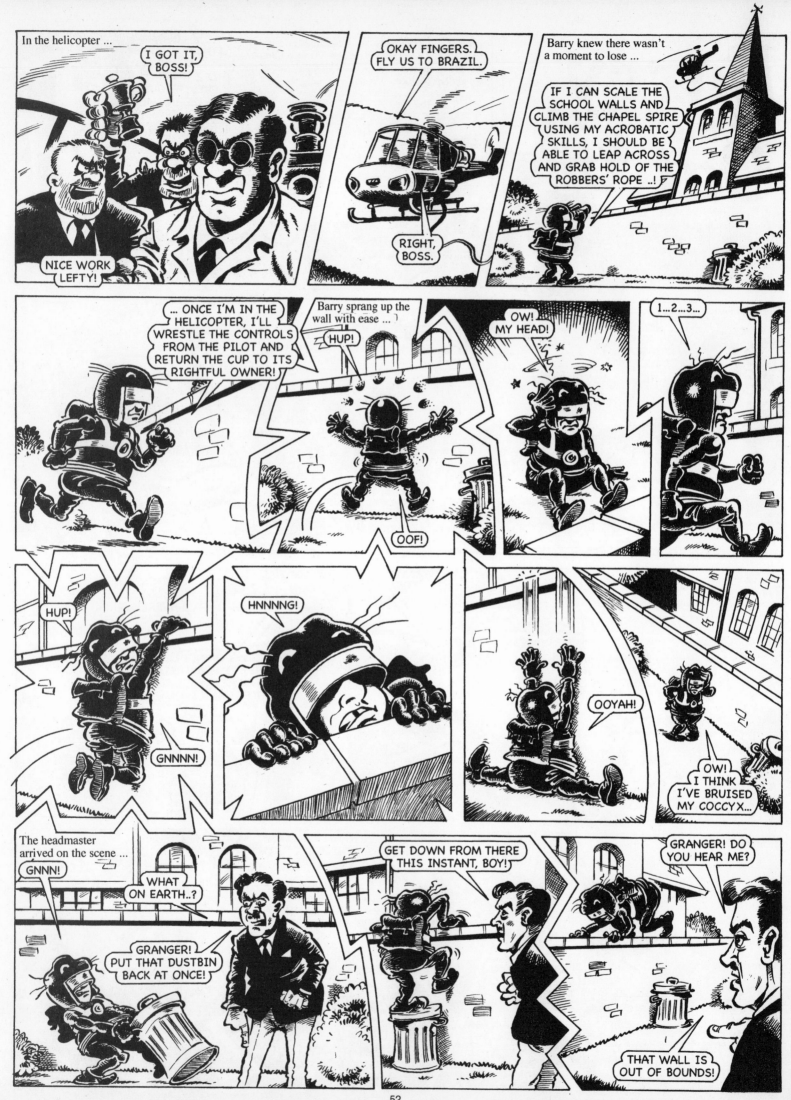

53

THE FORCES SWEETHEART IN...

KICK FOR VICTORY!

A TRUE-LIFE DAME VERA LYNN ADVENTURE

30TH JULY 1966, AND I HAD BEEN ASKED ALONG TO THE WORLD CUP FINAL AT WEMBLEY STADIUM TO ENTERTAIN THE ENGLAND SQUAD AT HALF-TIME. WHAT A MATCH IT WAS! THE CROWD WATCHED ENTHRALLED AS OUR BRAVE BOYS TOOK ON THE MIGHT OF THE GERMAN FOOTBALL MACHINE..

AFTER TWELVE MINUTES, THE FIRST BLOOD WAS DRAWN BY THE BOSCHE WHEN HELMUT HALLER FLUKED THE BALL INTO THE BACK OF OUR NET.

TAKE ZAT, HERR BANKS!

JAH! RICHT IN THE BACK OF ZE OLD ZWIEBELTASCHE!

BOO!

BAH! 1-NIL TO THE SAUSAGE EATERS.

BUT THEIR LEAD WAS SHORT LIVED, AS ONLY SEVEN MINUTES LATER GEOFF HURST SLAMMED A PILEDRIVER PAST THE HELPLESS GERMAN KEEPER.

GOR BLIMEY! WHAT A SMASHING GOAL, GEOFF! THAT'S ONE-ALL AND NO MISTAKE.

RUDDY GET IN!

DONNER UND BLITZEN! ICH BIN AS SICK AS EIN GROSSEWELLENSITTICH.

AND AS THE HALF-TIME WHISTLE BLEW, THERE WAS NOTHING BETWEEN THE TEAMS.

WELL, THAT'S THE FIRST FORTY-FIVE OVER, GEOFF.

YES. I'M FAIR LOOKING FORWARD TO DAME VERA LYNN AND MY HALF TIME ORANGE, SKIPPER.

THE MATCH WAS SHAPING UP FOR A THRILLING SECOND HALF, BUT LITTLE DID I KNOW THAT THE GERMAN MANAGER AND HIS COACH HAD A DIFFERENT GAMEPLAN IN MIND

I DON'T LIKE ZE LOOK OF ZIS GEOFF HURST. HE IS ZE DANGER MAN IN MEIN OPINION. HE COULD EASY GO ON TO SCORE EIN HATTENTRICKENSCHAFT.

DON'T WORRY, BOSS. ICH BIN INJECTED HIS HALF TIME ORANGE MIT NAZI CHEMICALS. HE VILL TAKE NICHT FURTHER PART IN ZIS GAME. HEH! HEH!

DURING THE INTERVAL, I KEPT OUR BOYS' MORALE UP WITH A SELECTION OF MY FAVOURITE SONGS.

♪ WE'LL MEET OVER, THE BLUEBIRDS OF DOVER, IN NIGHTINGALE SQUARE, JUST YOU WAIT AND SEE... ♪

BRINGS A TEAR TO YOUR EYE, DOESN'T IT, NOBBY?

I'LL SAY, SKIPPER.

FAIR MAKES YOU PROUD TO BE BRITISH, EH, GEOFF?

HNNNG!

WHAT IS IT? WHAT'S WRONG?

I DON'T...FEEL...TOO GOOD, SKIPPER...

...SUCH A PAIN...

WHAT'S GOING ON, MEN? WHY AREN'T YOU OUT ON THE FIELD? THE SECOND IS ABOUT TO START.

IT'S HURSTY, BOSS. HE'S IN A REAL BAD WAY.

AAARGH! CAN'T...FEEL MY...LEGS!

NO WONDER. LOOK AT THIS - HIS HALF TIME ORANGE HAS BEEN INJECTED WITH NAZI POISON!

WHAT ARE WE GOING TO DO, BOSS. WHO'S GOING TO GO OUT AND SCORE THE REST OF GEOFF'S HAT-TRICK?

NEVER...ON THE FIELD OF HUMAN FOOTBALL...HAS SO MUCH CHEATING BEEN PERPETRATED...BY SO FEW...IN FRONT OF SO MANY.

I KNEW MY MOMENT HAD COME...

I'LL DO IT, SIR ALF. I'LL STEP INTO HURSTY'S BOOTS.

YOU!?!

BUT DAME VERA, YOU'RE A MIDDLE AGED SINGER. WHAT DO YOU KNOW ABOUT FOOTBALL?

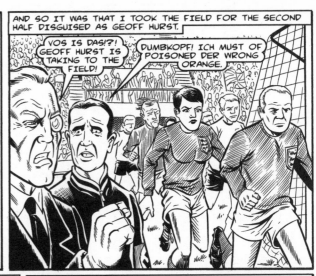

NANOOK of BREAKER BEACH

WHILST PLAYING WITH HIS PET SEAL UGRUK ON AN ICE FLOE AS A BABY, NANOOK NILAK HAD BEEN SWEPT OUT TO SEA. FOR MONTHS, THE PAIR HAD DRIFTED DOWN AMERICA'S WESTERN SEABOARD BEFORE WASHING UP ON CALIFORNIA'S BREAKER BEACH. THERE, LIVING IN SAND IGLOO WITH HIS FAITHFUL PINNIPED PET, NANOOK HAD GROWN UP ALONGSIDE THE LOCAL SURFER DUDES...

YOU GIRLS WAIT HERE. ME AND CHUCK ARE GONNA CATCH SOME WAVES.

HOT DIGGETY. LET'S HANG TEN, DUDE.

WOW! IT'S SCOTT AND CHUCK.

THEY'RE THE BEST SURFERS ON UM BREAKER BEACH.

CAN I UM JOIN YOU? I'VE HEARD THE SWELL'S GOING TO BE UM BITCHIN' TODAY.

WHAT, YOU? COME SURFING WITH US?

DREAM ON, YOU INUIT DWEEB.

HO! HO! WHAT A DORK!

YEAH! AWESOME TO THE MAX!

SIGH...COME ON, UGRUK.

LOOK AT THEM GO!

LET'S GET BACK TO UM FISHING FOR OUR TEA.

I SOMETIMES THINK WE'LL NEVER MAKE ANY FRIENDS HERE AT BREAKER BEACH.

EXCUSE ME...

HI, I'M BRANDY AND THESE ARE MY FRIENDS BOBBIE-SUE AND MARY-ERIC.

HI, I'M NANOOK...

WE'VE SEEN YOU SITTING OVER HERE ON YOUR OWN A LOT...

LISTEN, WE'RE HAVING A CLAM-BAKE ON THE BEACH THIS EVENING, AND WE WERE JUST WONDERING IF YOU WOULD...ERM...

UM YES?

GET THE HECK OUT OF HERE!

CLEAR OFF, YOU CANDLE MUNCHING FREAK!

YOU'RE SPOILING THE VIEW WITH THAT STUPID SAND HOUSE OF YOURS.

HO HO!

HA HA!

LATER THAT EVENING, AS THE SUN WENT DOWN, THE CLAM BAKE WAS IN FULL SWING. BUT NANOOK AND UGRUK COULD ONLY WATCH FROM THE DUNES.

THEY LOOK LIKE THEY ARE HAVING SO MUCH UM FUN.

THIS BEACH CLAM-BAKE IS AWESOME, BRO!

YES. IT'S ABSOLUTELY GNARLACIOUS, DUDE.

WELL, MAKE THE MOST OF IT, KIDS...

BUT THEN...

VWOOSH!

MY HAT! THE WIND'S TOOK MY HAT! JIMMINY CRICKETS! HELP!

OH MY GOD! IT'S BLOWN OUT TO SEA!

AND NOW IT'S BEEN GRABBED BY A KILLER WHALE!

PLEASE! MY HAT...SOMEONE DO SOMETHING!

SUDDENLY...

LOOK!

QUICK AS A FLASH, NANOOK TOOK TO THE SURF.

IT'S THAT ESKIMO GUY!

NANOOK PADDLED HIS WHALE BONE AND STITCHED SEALSKIN SURFBOARD OUT TO SEA WHERE, USING SKILLS LEARNT AT THE KNEES OF HIS FOREFATHERS, HE HUNTED DOWN THE LEVIATHAN.

THERE HE IS. IF I CAN JUST HANG UM TEN AND GET A LITTLE CLOSER.

I'VE GOT TO CATCH UP. IF THAT GREAT BEAST DIVES, THAT UM HAT IS LOST FOREVER.

MY GRANDFATHERS TAUGHT ME THAT UM KILLER WHALE IS UM MOST VULNERABLE BEHIND UM EYE.

WEEEEEK!

THUNK!

GOT IT!

SHORTLY.

HERE'S YOUR UM HAT, MR OYSTERBURGER.

THANK YOU, SON.

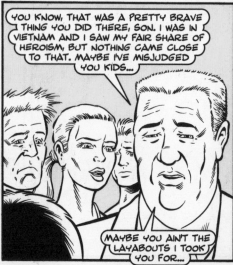

YOU KNOW, THAT WAS A PRETTY BRAVE THING YOU DID THERE, SON. I WAS IN VIETNAM AND I SAW MY FAIR SHARE OF HEROISM, BUT NOTHING CAME CLOSE TO THAT. MAYBE I'VE MISJUDGED YOU KIDS...

MAYBE YOU AIN'T THE LAYABOUTS I TOOK YOU FOR...

59

1 THE MOTOR workshop is traditionally a male-dominated environment, and as such can be a slightly intimidating place for a visiting female customer. To make women drivers feel more at home in the garage, these mechanics have thoughtfully put up a calendar featuring a picture of a pretty girl. This touch of femininity amidst a masculine environment is a good way to put lady customers at their ease.

MODERN CARS contain miles of wiring, and a simple electrical fault can be almost impossible to track down and remedy. Here, a customer has brought his car into the garage because the interior light in the boot has stopped coming on. The mechanic tells him he has located a short circuit in the car's expensive, state-of-the-art CD radio, which he has removed. This will later be recycled and sold on to another customer. The mechanic has also replaced the bulb in the boot light.

2 IN A traffic accident, it's often just the front or back of a car that is damaged beyond repair. Scrapping the whole car in these circumstances would be a waste of precious natural resources. Here, the ingenious motor engineer is welding together two such salvaged halves, in order to recycle their components into a perfectly good, brand new car which may give many months' service to an unsuspecting young family.

3 WHEN THEY fail, it can be uneconomic to replace certain large motor car components. This gearbox, for instance, is dangerously worn after many hundreds of thousands of miles of driving, but it would be prohibitively expensive to fit a new one. The canny mechanic decides that the best course of action is to "mend and make do", and fills it with sawdust. This simple, yet effective procedure, which makes the gearbox feel as good as new, will allow it to work smoothly once more, giving its owner up to several dozen miles of carefree motoring.

MANY CAR parts can be fitted to a number of different models made by the same manufacturer. Here, a customer has paid to have a brand new stainless steel exhaust pipe fitted to his family hatchback. However, the motor engineer fits the expensive new system to his own car, which is of the same make, and generously gives the customer his own, slightly used - yet still perfectly serviceable - exhaust at no extra charge.

A MODERN MOTOR CAR is a very complicated piece of machinery with thousands of moving parts. Gone are the days when, should it go wrong, we could tinker under the bonnet ourselves. Today we must take it to an expert - the Garage Mechanic. In many ways the garage mechanic is like a surgeon: he knows how to diagnose and cure the mechanical illnesses that affect our cars' systems. He has trained for many years to do his job and uses specialised tools to carry out complex procedures. And, like a surgeon, he also has the ability to take an arm and a leg off you.

Let's take a look behind the scenes at a typical motor engineer's garage.

WHEN any repair has been made, it is important that the motor mechanics test-drive the car to make sure it is functioning correctly and safely. This vehicle, which was brought in to have a new radiator fitted, has been thoroughly tested over the course of a weekend, being driven long distances at top speed over various terrains. Happily, it has passed with flying colours!

GARAGE MECHANICS like to belittle their customers by moving the driving seat as far back on its runners as is physically possible. This driver returns to pick up his vehicle and the mechanics gather to watch him pathetically having to slide his seat forwards until he can reach the pedals and steering wheel.

4 THIS MOTOR engineer is a perfectionist. He has decided that the brake pads on this woman's car, although practically brand new, need to be replaced. In order to avoid confusing the customer by showing her the actual pads from her car, he shows her a set of badly-worn brake pads from another vehicle.

5 BY LAW, contaminated fluids drained from vehicles must be collected by a registered disposal company. However, calling their lorry all the way out to the garage in order to collect a relatively small amount of used sump oil would create an unacceptable amount of pollution, causing global warming. So this environmentally-responsible mechanic does his bit to save the planet by tipping it down the drain.

6 SOME INTERMITTENT faults reported by customers don't show up during servicing. To find out the specific circumstances that led them to occur, this mechanic makes a phone call to a young woman who brought a car in which keeps losing power on hills. Like a detective, he has to know every detail of her driving style in order to diagnose the problem correctly and make the necessary repairs. He asks her whether she rests her hands on the gear lever whilst driving, whether she drives in high heel shoes and what colour knickers she is wearing.

7 DURING THEIR regular maintenance regime, many car owners fail to make routine checks on the spare tyre in their boot well. Here, the mechanic takes advantage of this fact by swapping this customer's brand new, spare alloy wheel for a barely-legal budget re-mould on a rusty steel rim. This good spare is fitted to another customer's car, making it safer on the road for everyone.

NEXT WEEK: People Who Help Us
The Estate Agent

The Adventures of
JASON
and the
Lagernauts

In Ancient Greece, many tales were told of brave adventurers. One such was Jason, who set sail with his brave crew on a quest to find the Golden Fleece, a pub far beyond the edge of the known world. Legend had it that there they would find a pint glass from which Zeus himself had quaffed Kestrel. It was said that this glass would never drain of lager, and that he who possessed it would have eternal dizziness.

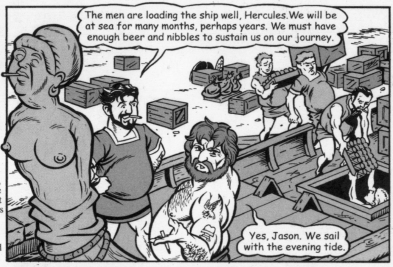

The men are loading the ship well, Hercules. We will be at sea for many months, perhaps years. We must have enough beer and nibbles to sustain us on our journey.

Yes, Jason. We sail with the evening tide.

So... Row, men. And may the Gods protect us. I'm just off to my cabin for a can or two.

Next morning...

By Apollo himself, my head is thumping. Time for the hair of the dog.

By the eyes of Mars! What has happened, Hercules?

The beer is all gone, Jason. To venture any further without any cans on board would be suicide...

The helmsman has the DTs. If we attempt to navigate through the Clashing Rocks, we will surely perish. We **must** turn back.

No, we cannot turn back. We would be heading into the sun and I couldn't cope with that, not with **this** fucking hangover.

But, Jason. What shall we do?

Suddenly...

Jason! Hercules! The Water...it's **moving!** Something's happening!

As the awestruck Lagernauts looked on, a huge figure rose out of the sea...

It's the end of the world! We are done for!

No, Hercules! It is **Gassius**, the God of fizzy lager...

We are saved!

Do not be afraid, Lagernauts. But hold fast for your very lives!

Gassius belched with the sound like a mighty crash of thunder, filling the ship's sails with wind and sending the Lagernauts swiftly and safely through the Clashing Rocks...

BURP!

Time passed, and a thick mist engulfed the ship. The Lagernauts began to grow restive

Are we not there, yet? I could murder a pint.

There's not a sip of beer to be had, we are lost in a mist as thick as a Welshman's cock and the dartboard's been washed over the side. Where are your precious Gods **now**, Jason?

Enough! Listen! What is that beautiful sound?

I hear nothing, save the creaking of the mast. Face it, Jason, without more pop, and maybe a few crisps or peanuts, we're doomed.

Hush! There it is again!

Sure enough, out of the fog came the entrancing sound of tins being opened...

Steady as she goes. Head for the heavenly music. By all the Gods on Mount Olympus, we shall feast on lager tonight!

HURRAH!!

About time. I've been shaking like a shitting dog.

Suddenly, a shout rang out...

Jason! The mists are parting!

Oh, no, **Harpies!** Helmsman, turn the boat about or we will be dashed to pieces upon the rocks.

Hercules had heard many tales of ships lured to their doom by the hypnotic sound of lager tins being opened. He heaved with all his might on the tiller.

Gertcha!

By Neptune! The ship is saved!

He has the beergut of **twenty men!**

Over the following months, Jason and the Lagernauts sailed across innumerable oceans, and had many strange and wonderous adventures...

...until they finally reached the island beyond the edge of the world, where it was said they would find the Golden Fleece, where the miraculous pint glass of their quest was behind the bar.

Praise the Gods! Our quest is almost at an end.

Ace! My throat's as dry as a Trojan Horse's fanny.

Now, brave warriors, our final challenge. We must battle the seven-headed doorman who guards the entrance.

You're not coming in here with sandals.

No-one gets in without a tie on

No swords. Order of the management.

You want trouble?

He's never twenty-one.

It's a twenty-one bar.

I'll give you trouble, son.

Come on, men! Let's fill him in!

Kick him when he's down!

Leave it! He's had enough.

Let us enter the Golden Fleece and claim our prize.

But...

Erm..it's shut.

Eh? It's gone half eleven. It should be open by now.

Can't see anybody. No...it's empty.

Hold on! Look at this.

CLOSED
for
REFURBISHMENT
Grand Re-opening as
O'GRADY's
Irish Theme Bar
Summer 2500BC
sorry for any
inconvenience

Bugger it!
What shall we do now?

Do not be downhearted, men. For I have heard tell of a wonderous pub, The Railway Arms, where drinking up time lasts for all eternity.

Where is it, Jason?

Tell us! TELL US!

It is at the foot of the Singing Mountains, across the Sea of Seven Perils, beyond the Island of Certain Death.

But we must beware! The landlord's wife, Barbara, is a hideous *Gorgon!*

Any man who casts his eyes upon her face without beer goggles will be turned into a pillar of salted peanuts.

LESBIANS are everywhere. On the internet, on DVDs and on the Fantasy Channel 10 minute freeview. We see them at stag parties, we can download pictures of them onto our mobiles, and we can see parts of them in ripped up magazines under hedges. We can even talk to bored ones on the phone for just £1 per minute. We are all fascinated by lesbians. *But how do they work?*

The lesbian body is miracle of nature, a finely-tuned machine perfectly adapted to its purpose of having sex with other lesbians. It is composed of many parts, each with its own function. But what are they and what do they do? Let's have a look inside and see...

How a Lesbian Works

SKIN The skin is the largest organ in a lesbian's body, and it is essential as a means of regulating her body temperature. Unlike heterosexual women, lesbians tend to feel hot a lot of the time, and so often remove their clothes when in pretend offices, the backs of stretch limosines or when sitting on sofas with other lesbians. Whilst indulging in naked lesbian sex, their body temperature can get even higher. If this happens, blood vessels near the surface of the lesbian's skin dilate, causing the lesbian to flush. In addition, glands in the dermis release perspiration, causing the lesbian's breasts, thighs and buttocks to glisten with sweat. The evaporation of this sweat causes a cooling effect, restoring her to a comfortable lesbian temperature of 98.4 degrees.

FINGERS Fingers are one of the most important parts of a lesbian's body. Sensitive nerve endings in the skin on her fingertips enable the lesbian to feel whether another lesbian's nipple she is touching is erect or not. Antagonistic pairs of muscles in the arms and hand can then be brought into play, allowing the lesbian to rub or tweak the nipple harder as required, until it stands up like a chapel hat peg. A lesbian's fingers are also capable of performing precise acts of manipulation, for example undoing fiddly clasps on bras. However, they are unable to operate the fastenings on stockings and suspender belts, which therefore tend to remain in place whilst lesbian sex is being performed.

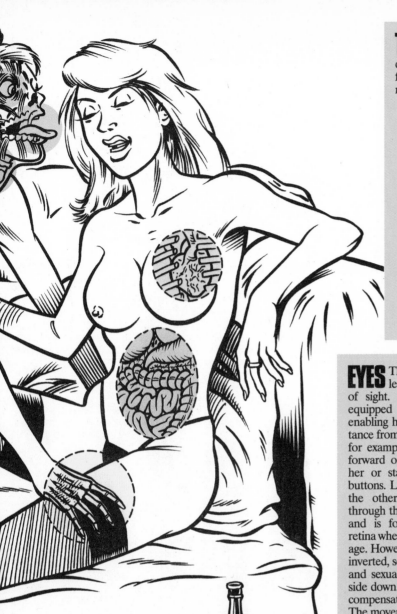

TONGUE
A lesbian's tongue has over 3000 taste buds which can identify sweet, sour, salty and bitter flavours. They enable the lesbian to distinguish between all the different things that she licks, such as nipples, fannies, fingertips and strap-on dildos. A lesbian's tongue also has a mass of interlinked muscles which allow it to be poked out of the side of her mouth during lesbian sex.

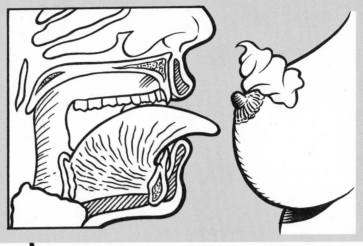

EYES
The eye is the lesbian's organ of sight. Each lesbian is equipped with two eyes, enabling her judge her distance from another lesbian, for example whilst leaning forward on a sofa to kiss her or start undoing her buttons. Light reflected off the other lesbian passes through the lens of the eye and is focused onto the retina where it forms an image. However, this image is inverted, so that the breasts and sexual organs are upside down. This visual signal passes down the lesbian's optic nerve into her brain, which compensates automatically by making the image of her lesbian partner the right way up. The movements of a lesbian's eyes are controlled by further pairs of antagonistic muscles, which allow them to be rolled back into their sockets at the height of her lesbian orgasms.

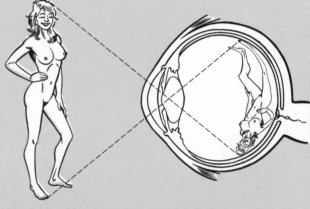

LARYNX
The sounds of lesbian sexual ecstasy are produced in the voicebox, or larynx, in the throat. Air from the lesbian's lungs causes the vocal cords to vibrate, and small muscles in the larynx alter the tension on the cords which alters the pitch of the orgasmic gasps and moans. The muscles of the jaws, lips and tongue, along with the roof of the mouth enable the lesbian to form words, like 'Oh, God!", "Yes! Yes! That's it!" and "Just there!"

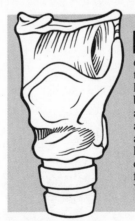

DIGESTIVE SYSTEM
Lesbians have a very limited diet, which mainly consists of whipped cream which they lick off the breasts of other lesbians. This is swallowed into the lesbian's stomach - where it is churned up and broken down with digestive juices. The residue passes into the small intestine, where it is further reduced with a mixture of lesbian bile and lesbian pancreatic fluid. Water is removed as the remaining material passes through the large intestine. The nutrients extracted from the cream during the digestive process provide essential energy for the lesbian's daily activities, such as clam jousting, dildo action and eating pussy.

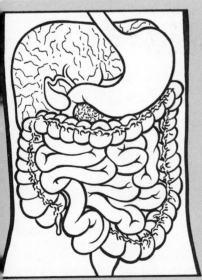

HEART
A lesbian's heart is a muscular pump about the size of a clenched fist, and it is situated in the chest between the lesbian's lungs. The heart's job is to pump oxygenated blood around the lesbian and to return deoxygenated blood to her lungs. At rest it beats around 70 times per minute, but during times of arousal, such as when a lesbian is engaged in breast fondling, french kissing on a sofa or mud wrestling, this rate increases.

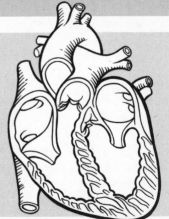

NEXT WEEK: People Who Help Us - The Nymphomaniac Nurse

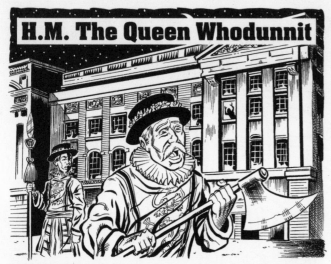

H.M. The Queen Whodunnit

NOVEMBER 1938. Despite the war clouds gathering over Europe, Britain slept soundly under the benign protection its beloved King George VI and his radiant wife Queen Elizabeth. Suddenly, the peaceful night air outside Buckingham Palace was shattered by a blood-curdling scream from the Queen's private dressing room. Awoken by the commotion, the members of the royal household rushed to see what had happened.

FIRST on the scene was 12-year-old Princess Elizabeth, who found her mother the Queen collapsed on the floor. "Mama! Mama! What happened?" she cried, cradling her mother's head. The majestic Princess craned forward to hear her mother's faint voice. "One of the footmen," the Queen gasped. "He brought me my evening gin and tonic... but as he left... he...he... he...didn't... didn't... *bow!*" As the horrifying words left her lips, the Queen lapsed into unconsciousness. "The Queen! The Queen! Somebody help my mother the Queen," screamed the little Princess.

THE unconscious Queen was carried to her bed and Palace Physician Sir Gladstone Gamble was summoned. The anxious King George was taken to one side as the doctor delivered his diagnosis. "Her majesty has suffered a terrible shock, sir," explained the medical man. "The horror of her experience has put her into a serious coma from which she may never awake. All we can do is wait and pray that she recovers," he added gravely. But little Lilibet was determined to identify the evil footman who had brought her beloved mother so close to death. "I shall find the footman responsible," she vowed. "I shall find him and make sure he is brought to justice."

AND Lillibet knew exactly where to start her search for the offending minion. "My mother, the Queen, said that the footman was bringing her gin when he committed the crime," she thought to herself. So off she set for the Queen's private gin cellar. It was below stairs, which was a part of the palace she had never been to before - the realm of servants and lackeys. The walls were stark and bare. There was not a piece of gold or velvet to be seen and she shuddered at the lack of opulence around her. But bravely she pressed on. And as she entered the cellar, lying on the floor by that day's gin supply she spotted a small slip of paper.

"GOSH! It's a betting slip," said Elizabeth as she examined the scrap of paper. "This must be a clue. It means that the footman who brought Mama's gin was the same one who took her betting slips to the bookmaker in Picadilly High Street." The little Princess had started to unravel the mystery. But which footman was it? She knew her Mother would never be able to identify him by sight, as all common people looked the same. She had to have a name.

ELIZABETH decided she had to speak to the bookie. Apart from giving orders to servants, she had never spoken to a member of the lower orders before, and the thought made her feel physically sick. But she was a plucky princess and blue Windsor blood coursed through her veins. She took control of herself and, head high, walked into the den of commoners.

INSIDE, Elizabeth strode to the counter. Realising who she was, the bookmaker bowed low, quivering before her regal majesty. "Your R.. R.. Royal Highness," he stammered. "What an honour." Elizabeth looked at him with disgust. His watch was gold-plated, and his shirt, although clean, clearly cost less than a hundred guineas. She felt her gorge rise. "Who placed a bet here yesterday for my Mama, Her Majesty the Queen?" she demanded haughtily. "I... I don't know, you Highness," he replied. "A... a... footman. He didn't tell me his name. But I do remember that he appeared to be in some pain. He said something about his bad back playing up."

LILLIBET was now faced with the prospect of having to pay another visit to a commoner. The doctor who treated the palace footmen for their aches and pains would provide the final piece of the jigsaw. "I want to see all your medical records," she proclaimed as she burst through the door. "I am sorry your Highness," ventured the doctor. "Medical records are private and may not be seen, not even by the highest in the land." The little princess was outraged. Never had she encountered such disrespect and insolence!

"BOW! BOW to your future Sovereign!" she hollered with regal dignity. "And do NOT rise until I, Princess Elizabeth, give my Royal permission." Such was the majesty of her voice, that the doctor did immediately as he was commanded. And as the physician stood in a respectful stoop, Lillibet stepped lightly over to the filing cabinet and began to go through his confidential records. A minute's searching was all it took. She finally had her answer.

BACK AT Buckingham Palace, the plucky little Princess ran straight to her mother's bed chamber where her father the King was keeping a vigil by her bed. "Mama, Mama," she whispered. "I have found the identity of the footman who did this to you." Both the king and Lillibet saw the faintest glimmer of a smile play across the Queen's majestic lips and her regal eyelids flickered. The King looked at his daughter with pride. "I think she's going to be alright, Lillibet," he said. "Thanks to you, my little princess."

AN HOUR later, the future Queen summoned the palace staff to the Great Hall. Traditionally used for entertaining the crowned heads of Europe, this magnificent room was now to be used to unmask a criminal. Elizabeth held the crowd in her thrall as she explained how the perpetrator of the crime had the betting slip, and how she had subsequently discovered he had a bad back. And she revealed that a search through the medical records showed a footman had visited his doctor with back pain that same day. "Step forward, Albert Pastry," she called. An old, bent footman timidly approached her.

PASTRY, who had been in the employment of the Royal Family since he was 2 years old, immediately confessed. He explained that crippling lumbar arthritis that caused excruciating pain whenever he bent, and he cravenly begged their Majesties' forgiveness. "What shall we do, Lillibet?" asked the King. "As you discovered him, you shall sentence him." Elizabeth showed the compassion and empathy with the common people that would in future serve her well as Queen. "I think he should be given a chance," she said with a gracious smile. So, after breakfast the following day, the footman was given a three minute head start before the Palace Hunt chased him down and tore him to pieces.

Incredible Flying Machines

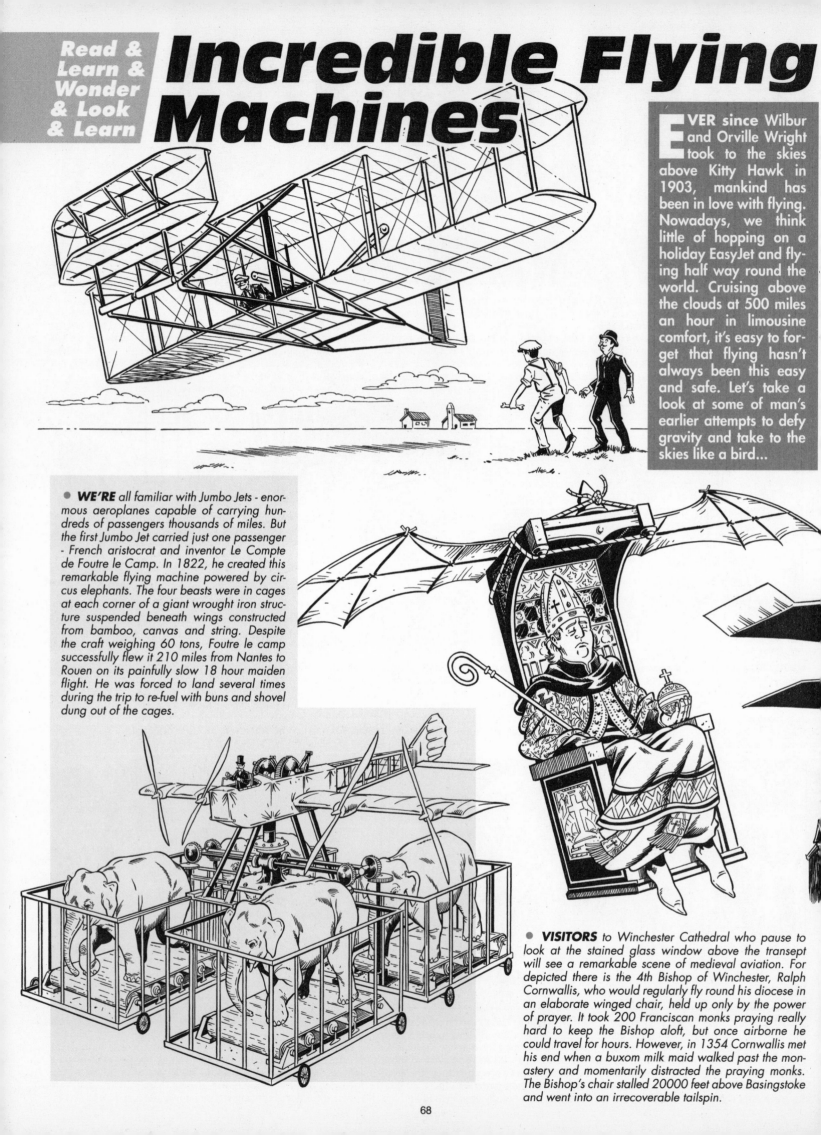

EVER since Wilbur and Orville Wright took to the skies above Kitty Hawk in 1903, mankind has been in love with flying. Nowadays, we think little of hopping on a holiday EasyJet and flying half way round the world. Cruising above the clouds at 500 miles an hour in limousine comfort, it's easy to forget that flying hasn't always been this easy and safe. Let's take a look at some of man's earlier attempts to defy gravity and take to the skies like a bird...

● **WE'RE** all familiar with Jumbo Jets - enormous aeroplanes capable of carrying hundreds of passengers thousands of miles. But the first Jumbo Jet carried just one passenger - French aristocrat and inventor Le Compte de Foutre le Camp. In 1822, he created this remarkable flying machine powered by circus elephants. The four beasts were in cages at each corner of a giant wrought iron structure suspended beneath wings constructed from bamboo, canvas and string. Despite the craft weighing 60 tons, Foutre le camp successfully flew it 210 miles from Nantes to Rouen on its painfully slow 18 hour maiden flight. He was forced to land several times during the trip to re-fuel with buns and shovel dung out of the cages.

● **VISITORS** to Winchester Cathedral who pause to look at the stained glass window above the transept will see a remarkable scene of medieval aviation. For depicted there is the 4th Bishop of Winchester, Ralph Cornwallis, who would regularly fly round his diocese in an elaborate winged chair, held up only by the power of prayer. It took 200 Franciscan monks praying really hard to keep the Bishop aloft, but once airborne he could travel for hours. However, in 1354 Cornwallis met his end when a buxom milk maid walked past the monastery and momentarily distracted the praying monks. The Bishop's chair stalled 20000 feet above Basingstoke and went into an irrecoverable tailspin.

● **IN** 1851, The Daily Telegraph offered a prize of three shillings (over £65 billion in today's money) for the first person to successfully reach America by air. In an attempt to win the prize, Dafydd Prestatyn, a blacksmith from Llanfairfechan constructed an enormous wrought-iron catapult, with which to propel himself the 3000 miles across the Atlantic. He situated the machine on the cliffs at Holyhead, and on the 4th October, sitting on a little leather seat on the elastic, was pulled back as far as Nottingham by a traction engine. When released, Prestatyn flew towards America at the speed of a bullet. Four hours later, he crashed through the roof of a greenhouse in Newfoundland. His celebration was short-lived. The Telegraph refused to pay as Newfoundland was a province of Canada, not America. A disillusioned Prestatyn returned to Wales where he turned to drink and died penniless.

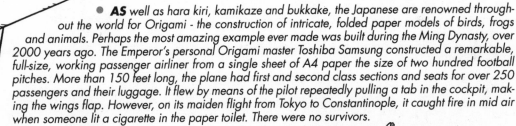

● **MOST** successful rock stars spend their millions on fast cars, fancy houses and drugs. But not Geordie songsmith Sting. For in 2004, the former Police frontman announced that he had sunk all his record royalties into developing the world's first tantric sex-powered helicopter. In a demonstration before the world's press, Sting and his wife Trudi Styler climbed into the cockpit of the high-tech craft and began having sex. Carbon fibre cranks attached to the singer's buttocks and running through a revolutionary low friction gearbox to titanium rotors quickly got the machine airborne. Using ancient tantric sex techniques to delay orgasm, the twat was able to keep his aircraft in flight for five hours. However, disaster struck when Styler unexpectedly tickled her hubby's nuts causing him to go off. The machine lost all power and plummeted 300 feet into the crowd below where it exploded in a giant ball of flame, killing 58 and maiming hundreds more. Fortunately, Sting escaped with just minor bruising and a scorched bell end.

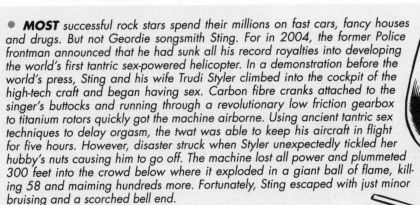

● **AS** well as hara kiri, kamikaze and bukkake, the Japanese are renowned throughout the world for Origami - the construction of intricate, folded paper models of birds, frogs and animals. Perhaps the most amazing example ever made was built during the Ming Dynasty, over 2000 years ago. The Emperor's personal Origami master Toshiba Samsung constructed a remarkable, full-size, working passenger airliner from a single sheet of A4 paper the size of two hundred football pitches. More than 150 feet long, the plane had first and second class sections and seats for over 250 passengers and their luggage. It flew by means of the pilot repeatedly pulling a tab in the cockpit, making the wings flap. However, on its maiden flight from Tokyo to Constantinople, it caught fire in mid air when someone lit a cigarette in the paper toilet. There were no survivors.

● **MANY** people know that submarines were first used by the Confederate side in the American Civil War. However, few realise that the same army also attempted to bring aircraft into the conflict. In 1863, General "Stonewall" Jackson ordered the construction of an experimental iron bumble bee, which he intended to use against Union forces amassed on the banks of the Potomac. Two soldiers were riveted into the craft where they turned handles connected to short, brass wings. In an attempt to replicate the flying technique of the insect, the mechanism was geared such that one turn of the hand-crank would produce 10,000 beats of each wing. But the machine never got airborne. Instead, it simply spun round on the floor in circles, buzzing loudly for twenty minutes until the exhausted men inside suffocated. Why didn't it work? Jackson never knew, and to this day it remains a mystery. The world's cleverest boffins still haven't got a clue how bees get off the ground!

Next Week in Read & Learn & Wonder & Look & Learn:
Dildos through the Ages.

NEXT WEEK - JIMBO JUMBO AND HIS ROBO JOBOS FOIL A FARMER'S EVIL PLAN TO DELIVER A CHRISTMAS TREE TO THE LOCAL ORPHANAGE.

Who's Who at a Motor Car Race

AS EVERY heterosexual boy knows, the most exciting place on earth to be is a motor car race. But the spectacle of seeing the drivers race round the track at a hundred miles per hour and crashing in a gigantic ball of flames is only half the story. What you might not realise is that the activity behind the scenes is often just as exciting as the race itself.

Lets take a stroll down the pit lane at a motor car race where we'll meet lots of people with fascinating jobs. Once again, it's time to look and read and learn and wonder...

(All references correct at time of going to press in 2002)

The Commentator   1
Without a commentator, watching a motor car race on your television set would be a confusing business. You would have no idea which of the brightly coloured cars streaking past the camera was in the lead. Without his expert commentary, it would be all too easy to mistake one car for another, or to completely miss an important piece of the action.

The
The pu
employ
also lias
advert b
the race.

The Number One Driver   6
At the wheel of each team's best-prepared car is their number one driver, who can earn upwards of £20 million each year. He is so well rewarded because there are only a handful of men in the World capable of driving a car round in circles for a couple of hours every other Sunday. But his life is not all glamour and excitement. He spends a lot of time visiting sponsors, testing cars and making heavily-publicised hospital trips to visit mechanics he has ran over.

The Nur
He is the te
drives exactl
not quite as f
ning a race, it
with his gearbo
highly paid tea
sibility, because

The Fan   11
Die-hard fan travels thousands of miles and spends £300 to sit in a plastic seat which affords him perhaps the worst view on the planet of the events taking place. He shouts tactical words of encouragement to his favourite drivers who, passing him at breakneck speed with their ears six inches from a 1000 horsepower engine, couldn't hear their own nads explode, let alone his pathetic yelpings from row Z.

Celebrity Fa
The danger and e
irresistible allure f
Stallone, Paul New
William, the Krankie
only a few of the fan
seen getting under th
things they shouldn't

2
ex-racing driver himself, is
commentator's mistakes. He
director to ensure that the
ith the most exciting parts of

The Chief Mechanic 3
The chief mechanic is responsible for ensuring that his cars are equipped with the very latest technical developments, and for hiding them so his team isn't disqualified. He will usually only stay with a motor racing team for a couple of seasons before moving on, selling his skills - and as many parts and top secret plans as he can stuff into his overalls - to the highest bidder.

Second Mechanic 4
He is the head of the pit crew, and it is his job to force 50 gallons of highly unstable rocket fuel into a white hot engine in 4 seconds, using a 200lb locking nozzle as easy to get on and off as a bra, whilst wearing thick steel and asbestos mittens. He earns about £200 a week.

The Dead Mechanic 5
In the excitement of a race, drivers may often inadvertantly run over and maim or kill their mechanics. Tragically, such an accident can add as much as 2 or 3 seconds to a pit-stop.

7
river
umber one driver, and he
s his colleague, though
tally finds himself win-
tend he's having trouble
ugh to allow his more
ast. It's a great respon-
this he is sacked.

The Driver's Wife 8
A motor race is a magnet for beautiful women, and none is more beautiful than the driver's wife. She provides a welcome touch of glamour as the camera zooms in on her anxious face as she watches a doctor's frantic attempts to restart her husband's heart whilst a marshall retrieves his head from a bush.

The British Driver 9
Like all British sportsmen, he is a lovable loser; it's a moral victory for him to get through the first corner. Don't bother looking out for him on the podium, but you can see him getting his testicles felt by Jonathan Ross on 'They Think It's All Over', or as Widow Twanky in Aladdin at the Sunderland Empire.

Helicopter TV Crew 10
A recent addition to motor racing coverage on the television, the helicopter TV crew remains airborne throughout the entire race. Receiving their instructions from the director, they are able to hover above the track to ensure they get the most exciting shots of the doctor's frantic attempts to restart a driver's heart and the marshall retrieving his head from a bush.

12
motor race exerts an
megastars. Sylvester
mpbell, Prince
out of Mud are
to be regularly
et and touching
grid.

The TV Anchor Man 13
It is his job to travel half way round the world to spend twenty minutes summing up the three hours of yawning inaction which the television audience has just endured. Before the race, he has to ask his panel of experts how the British driver will perform. Afterwards, he has to ask them where they think it all went wrong for the British driver. Usually the first corner.

The Supremo 14
The supremo is surely the luckiest man in the World. He's a multi-billionaire, he's got the biggest Scalextric set on Earth, and his wife's bosoms are directly level with his face.

The Sponsor 15
A motor racing team is extremely costly to run: a modern racing car can cost thousands of pounds. On top of this, every time a driver goes up in a fireball, his team can be left with lots of unsaleable merchandise. The sponsor bears the brunt of the team's everyday costs. In return, the logo of his cigarette company is displayed absolutely everywhere, from the car itself, to team merchandise such as children's T-shirts, children's baseball caps and babies' bibs.

Next week....
Behind the scenes at a Brazilian snuff movie

The Diary of Samuel L. Pepys

Thursday September 17th

*1. **I did arise by five**, before day, and went to market to buy fowle and lamprey for dinner with Rear Admiral Kempthorne, his lady and his young cozens this night. Sweet bitches alright.*

*2. **At market** I had cause to speke roughly with one trader. Near twenty shillings for a sack posset and a dish of anchovies! Had to stand on the motherfucker's head so he could hear me better.*

*3. **To the admiralty**, there to attend a court martial of Captain Middleton. Lord, to hear of his rogueries and wretched doings! Popped a cap in his knee for his cheeke.*

*4. **Thence home**. And cooke come to prepare of dinner. Fat-assed motherfucker did reeke of wines and ales such that I caused to teach him his misgivings by boyling his unrighteous head.*

*5. **Evening**, and Rear Admiral Kempthorne come with his wife and, to my great content, his two cozens, whom I found to be of excellent discourse with titties to beat the motherfucking band.*

*6. **Dinner** was noble enough and my lady Emma did sing most finely so as to ravish us. Young Rose put her hand beneath the table to rest on my britches and therein, my dick.*

Samuel L. Pepys was a highly respected member of court and government in 17th century London. He rose to become secretary of the Admiralty, and even did some time up the big house for alleged complicity in a plot to whack the Pope, surviving to become president of the Royal Society. A Bad Motherfucker, Pepys' diaries have supplied historians with the word on what shit went down with the highlife and lowlife of the capital in turbulent times - the plague, the great fire, the dope drought of '59 - all are documented in his faithful journal, giving us a true flavour of the situation around being a society brother in the big bad city. However, it wasn't all whores with sores and crap floating in the damn street. There was some fine pussy and grade A shit to be located if a brother kept himself on the good foot and looked after his moves.

7. *The Admiral* and his wife and I did withdrawe for port and to eat of fruits. Rose and Emma sat to sew and I to join them. To my great content, they smoke the bone with my barely asking.

8. *Rear Admiral* Kempthorne did spoil our mirth in bare five minutes. Red like a Kentish strawberry the brother chances to roar at my countenance and utter such words as are rarely heard!

9. *Afore I could* calm myself, I have ventured my flintlock into the old man's mouth. Thence to teach him of his rough ways and how he should not push his face to mine thusly.

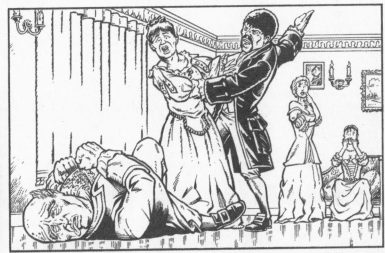

10. *The fat man's* heart gives out presently. The Rear Admiral expires. His wife comes thither to find a scene and becomes shrill and undone. I need to slap some shush into her ugly face.

11. *My Lord* enjoys a moonlit swim from the chamber window. My lady continues in disarray wailing and lamenting of her late husband. I shoot the bitch out of God-damned principle.

12. *My ladies* Rose and Emma seem saddened, but are content once more on learning my lordship's legacy will make them the richest bitches in Southwark. And so to bed.

FLUSH GORDON
SPACE PLUMBER OF THE FUTURE

2020 AD. ORBITING 150 MILES ABOVE THE EARTH, THE FLOATING CITY OF SKYTROPOLIS IS HOSTING A MEETING OF THE INTERGALACTIC FEDERATION. IT IS AN HISTORIC EVENT, AS THE HEADS OF ALL THE WARRING PLANETS HAVE COME TOGETHER TO FORMULATE AND SIGN AN ACCORD THAT WILL LEAD TO A LASTING PEACE THROUGHOUT THE UNIVERSE.

INSIDE SKYTROPOLIS SPACE PORT HOTEL, RECEPTIONIST AURORA AUSTRALIS IS WELCOMING THE DELEGATES.

SKYTROPOLIS WELCOMES ALL THE INTERGALACTIC FEDERATION DELEGATES

WELCOME TO SKYTROPOLIS, AMBASSADOR ZARGOS.

THANK YOU. I'M PLEASED TO BE HERE. THIS CONFERENCE IS A UNIQUE OPPORTUNITY...

...TO END LIGHT YEARS OF WARFARE BETWEEN THE GALAXIES AND BRING LASTING PEACE TO OUR SOLAR SYSTEM.

YOU ARE ON LEVEL 256, AMBASSADOR. THE ROBOT BELL HOP WILL SHOW YOU TO YOUR SUITE.

THANK YOU.

BUT NEARBY, IN AN IMPERIAL BATTLE CRUISER FROM THE PLANET ZONGO...

BY THE TWIN MOONS OF ZONGO, THIS PEACE CONFERENCE MUST BE STOPPED!

FOR MILLENNIA, MY PLANET HAS PROVIDED WEAPONS SO THAT THESE LESSER BEINGS COULD DESTROY EACH OTHER. IF THESE INTERGALACTIC WARS END THEN I...

...ZONG THE HEARTLESS, SHALL BE ROBBED OF MY POWER. IT IS TIME TO SCUPPER THE CONFERENCE

MY TURDATRON RAY WILL BLOCK EVERY LAVATORY ON SKYTROPOLIS! WITHOUT ADEQUATE PROVISION FOR THE REMOVAL OF FAECES AND URINE, CONDITIONS WILL BECOME UNBEARABLE, AND DELEGATES WILL BE FORCED TO LEAVE BEFORE THE PEACE CONCORD HAS BEEN FINALISED!

BWA! HA! HA! HA! HA! HA!

BWA! HA! HA! HA! HA! HA!

THE TOILET IN MY ROOM IS BLOCKED. PLEASE SORT IT OUT IMMEDIATELY.

YES, AMBASSADOR.

MY BOG'S BACKING UP TOO. THE PAN IS FULL OF POPS!

RIGHT AWAY, SIR.

HEY! I WAS HERE FIRST. WAIT YOUR TURN.

I CAN'T WAIT. YOU'VE OBVIOUSLY NEVER SMELLED MY SPECIES'S BM'S.

SUDDENLY...

ATTENTION DELEGATES OF THE FEDERATION. I AM ZONG THE HEARTLESS. YOUR EXCREMENT REMOVAL SYSTEM IS UNDER THE CONTROL OF MY TURDATRON RAY...

WHAT THE...?

THIS IS AN OUTRAGE!

YOUR PUNY ATTEMPTS TO SECURE AN INTERGALACTIC PEACE ARE FUTILE. YOUR AIMS CAN NEVER BE ACHIEVED WHILE YOUR CHOD BINS ARE ALL BUNGED UP WITH BANGERS AND MASH. RETURN TO YOUR PLANETS AND CONTINUE WAGING YOUR WARS!

PERHAPS HE'S RIGHT.

HMM! MAYBE WE WERE FOOLISH TO THINK WE COULD SECURE LASTING HARMONY.

WHAT ARE WE GOING TO DO? THE ENTIRE SKYTROPOLIS SEWERAGE SYSTEM HAS GONE INTO MELTDOWN AND THE PEACE CONFERENCE LOOKS LIKE IT WILL DISINTEGRATE.

YES.

SHORTLY, ON PLANET EARTH.

BEEP! BEEP! BEEP! BEEP! BEEP!

FLUSH GORDON
SPACE PLUMBER
No job too BIG or too Small

I WONDER WHO THAT COULD BE ON THE VIDEOPHONE?

DAILY UNIVERSE
GALACTIC PEACE CONFERENCE STARTS TODAY

SPACE COURT FOR PETE DOHERTY

BABYSHAMBLES FRONTMAN COULD GO TO PRISON THIS TIME

FLUSH GORDON, SPACE PLUMBER.

IT'S SKYTROPOLIS...WE'VE BEEN ATTACKED BY ZONG THE HEARTLESS...HE'S BLOCKED ALL OUR TOILETS...

...AND THE MEETING'S IN DANGER OF COLLAPSE! PLEASE HELP!

STAY RIGHT WHERE YOU ARE.

I'LL BE THERE IN FIVE MINUTES.

FOUR AND A HALF HOURS LATER...

FLUSH GORDON! THANK GOODNESS YOU'VE ARRIVED. SOME OF THE DELEGATES ARE PACKING THEIR BAGS.

DON'T WORRY. WHERE'S YOUR MAIN WASTE PODULE?

IT'S DOWN HERE. FOLLOW ME.

THIS IS IT!

RIGHT, LET ME SEE.

THIS DOESN'T LOOK GOOD. ZONG'S RAY HAS REVERSED THE POLARITY ON YOUR MAIN FOULAGE EXCHANGE PUMP MATRIX...

...EVERY FLUSH PUSHES MORE CRAP AND PISS UP THE U-BENDS!

AND HE'S IMMOBILIZED THE SAFETY BYPASS VALVES.

GASP! YOU MEAN...?

YES. IT COULD BLOW ANY SECOND...

...AND IF THAT HAPPENS, THE WHOLE OF SKYTROPOLIS COULD BE AWASH WITH EXTRA-TERRESTRIAL RICHARD THE THIRDS AND GYPSY'S KISS.

NOT TO MENTION BLOBS AND JAMRAGS. CAN YOU FIX IT, FLUSH?

HNNG! NO, I...CAN'T REVERSE IT AGAIN...HNNG!...THE BEAM IS TOO...HNNG!...STRONG!

THE ONLY WAY TO FIX THIS IS TO STOP ZONG'S BEAM.

HOW CAN YOU DO THAT?

I THINK I KNOW A WAY.

ZONG'S IMPERIAL BATTLE CRUISER IS POWERED BY A PROTON ACCELERATOR...

...IF I COULD GET ABOARD AND SOMEHOW DIVERT THE MAIN FOULPIPE FROM HIS LAVATORIES INTO THE IMPULSE GENERATOR...

...ONCE A FEW TURDS HIT THE ANTI-MATTER REACTOR CORE, THERE'LL BE A FIREWORK SHOW LIKE YOU'VE NEVER SEEN BEFORE.

WELL, I'M COMING WITH YOU, FLUSH. YOU'LL NEED ALL THE HELP YOU CAN GET...

...YOU'VE ONLY GOT 45 MINUTES TO SAVE THE UNIVERSE.

79

CONTINUED OVER

THE BEE MAN OF BIG BEN

LONDON, 1941, AND THE BLITZ IS AT ITS HEIGHT.

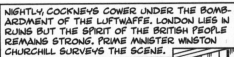

NIGHTLY, COCKNEYS COWER UNDER THE BOMBARDMENT OF THE LUFTWAFFE. LONDON LIES IN RUINS BUT THE SPIRIT OF THE BRITISH PEOPLE REMAINS STRONG. PRIME MINISTER WINSTON CHURCHILL SURVEYS THE SCENE.

SHOREDITCH, PIMLICO AND HACKNEY MARSHES WERE HIT LAST NIGHT, SIR. ANOTHER 10,000 DEAD.

GRIM TIDINGS, INDEED.

THERE IS SOME GOOD NEWS, SIR. THE MET. OFFICE FORECASTS SUNNY WEATHER FOR THE KING'S GARDEN PARTY AT BUCKINGHAM PALACE TOMORROW.

SPLENDID!

IT'LL BE THE SOCIAL EVENT OF THE WAR. EVERYONE WILL BE THERE - NOEL COWARD, IVOR NOVELLO, BENJAMIN BRITTEN. EVEN FRUITY METCALFE IS COMING OVER FROM BERMUDA.

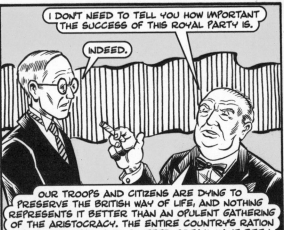

I DON'T NEED TO TELL YOU HOW IMPORTANT THE SUCCESS OF THIS ROYAL PARTY IS.

INDEED.

OUR TROOPS AND CITIZENS ARE DYING TO PRESERVE THE BRITISH WAY OF LIFE, AND NOTHING REPRESENTS IT BETTER THAN AN OPULENT GATHERING OF THE ARISTOCRACY. THE ENTIRE COUNTRY'S RATION OF BUTTER, JAM AND CLOTTED CREAM HAVE BEEN REQUISITIONED TO ENSURE THAT THIS GLITTERING EVENT IS A SUCCESS...

...IF WE ALLOW THE FUHRER TO DISRUPT IT, OUR BOYS AT THE FRONT MAY LOSE HEART. THEY MIGHT FEEL THERE'S NOTHING WORTH FIGHTING FOR.

LET'S PRAY THAT NOTHING GOES WRONG, PRIME MINISTER.

SUDDENLY...

WHAT'S THE MEANING OF THIS INTERRUPTION?

I'M SORRY, PRIME MINISTER, BUT THIS COULDN'T WAIT.

OUR CODE BREAKERS AT BLETCHLEY PARK HAVE INTERCEPTED THIS SET OF TOP SECRET PLANS. THE LUFTWAFFE HAVE A TERRIFYING NEW WEAPON.

WHAT IS IT?

A SQUADRON OF GIANT NAZI ROBOT WASPS. AND THEY ARE GOING TO UNLEASH THEM TOMORROW...AGAINST THE KING'S GARDEN PARTY.

OH MY GOD!

THEY HAVE ORDERS TO BUZZ ANNOYINGLY ROUND THE GUESTS, LAND ON SCONES, SWARM AROUND THE BUFFET TABLES AND PERHAPS STING AN ARISTOCRATIC GUEST OR TWO.

DAMN THEM! HOW LIKE THE BOSCHE TO WANT TO SPOIL A LOVELY AFTERNOON. WE MUST GO AND SEE THE ONLY MAN WHO CAN HELP...OUR COUNTRY'S MOST BRILLIANT INVENTOR.

WITHIN THE HOUR, CHURCHILL WAS ARRIVING AT PORTON DOWN, WHERE HE WAS TO MEET PROFESSOR EDGAR BARNES-NOBLE.

PORTON DOWN TOP SECRET WEAPONS ESTABLISHMENT

AH, PRIME MINISTER. WHAT BRINGS YOU HERE?

THE GRAVEST CIRCUMSTANCES, PROFESSOR BARNES-NOBLE. A THREAT OF DISRUPTION TO THE KING'S GARDEN PARTY TOMORROW.

THE PM QUICKLY BROUGHT THE BOFFIN UP TO SPEED ABOUT THE THREAT POSED BY THE GIANT NAZI ROBOT WASP SQUADRON.

SHORTLY.

HMMM! GIANT NAZI ROBOT WASPS, EH?

INDEED. WHAT'S TO BE DONE, PROFESSOR?

PRIME MINISTER, WHEN A BUILDING IS ON FIRE, WHAT DO WE USE TO PUT IT OUT?

WHY, WATER, OF COURSE. BUT I DON'T SEE...

BEAR WITH ME, SIR....

People Who Help Us...

This week: The Doctor

1. IT IS 6.00am, and the day has begun for our doctor, after a mere 5 hours sleep. An important late meeting in a lap-dancing club with a drug company rep has left him exhausted. Today he may be asked to make several life or death decisions, so it's into his clinic for a quick cocktail of dihydrocodeine, tilidine, tolfenamic acid, pyritinol and chloromethiazole out of the restricted drugs cabinet. This immediately perks him up and leaves him ready to face the day.

2. THUS refreshed, the doctor sets off for the first appointment in his busy schedule. The modern physician not only practises from his surgery, he more likely than not will be expected to appear on BBC Breakfast or GMTV where he will be called upon to comment about topical medical matters. Obesity, alcoholism and the mental state of Britney Spears are all subjects upon which he could be asked to give an opinion at a moment's notice.

3. IT IS stressful work speaking on live TV about a subject of which you have barely a passing knowledge. So our medic makes his way from the TV studio to the golf course for a relaxing nine holes. Doctors are asked to make life and death decisions every day of their working lives, and a tired mind is more likely to make mistakes than a fresh one. To make sure that his relaxation is not interrupted, he switches off his pager and his mobile phone.

4. AS WELL as medical practice, doctors must handle a lot of administrative work. Here he attends a working lunch with a drug rep at a posh restaurant. It is the job of the rep to persuade the doctor, by any means, that his company's products are effective. Sometimes they hold seminars at swanky hotels in Barbados with championship golf courses attached, which doctors attend to consider the benefits to their patients that a new drug could provide.

5. WHILST on call, our doctor could be asked to attend an emergency at a patient's home at any time, so it is vitally important that he has a fast, reliable car to get him there. For patient safety, the practice provides the doctor with a brand new BMW M5. And in order that he arrives relaxed and able to make split second life or death decisions, he opts for the full factory burr walnut pack, 16-speaker stereo and leather interior. And a matching Z8 convertible for his wife.

6. IT IS time for the doctor's first clinic of the day. The National Health Service is an over burdened institution, so today's modern doctor helps to take the strain off the service by seeing patients in a private clinic. Because these pay for their treatment, there is more money in the NHS budget for when the doctor finally gets round to seeing everybody else. This is the doctor's way of repaying the public, who paid for his expensive training through their taxes.

7. THE doctor is beginning to feel the mental strain of taking two or three private consultations. Stress can lead to a mis-diagnosis with serious or possibly even fatal results, so before he sees any more cases, it is important that the doctor winds down. For the sake of his patients, it's off to the driving range to relieve the tension of his demanding profession by hitting a couple of baskets of balls, followed by a relaxing drink in the golf club members' bar with colleagues.

8. SUITABLY refreshed, our doctor makes his way back to the hospital. But there is no time to see any patients. Most doctors these days churn out dire, formulaic medical columns for newspapers, and our doctor must dictate his work quickly in order to meet his paper's tight deadlines. An ability to look up information on erectile dysfunction, vaginisimus and G-spots on Wikipedia is needed to fill the titilating column inches relentlessly demanded by today's tabloid editors.

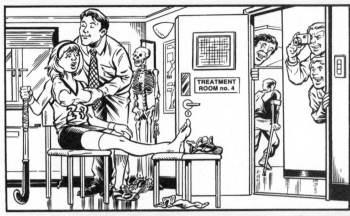

9. LIKE all of us, doctors are human and can make mistakes, but their mistakes could mean the difference between life and death. So it is vitally important that nothing is overlooked. At this Sports Injury Clinic, a young woman has what looks like a simple twisted ankle, but the doctor wants to make sure there have been no potentially serious injuries to her breasts. He examines them, but such is his thoroughness, he invites several colleagues in to give a second opinion.

10. THERE are not enough hours in the day for a busy doctor to meet all the demands that are placed on him. For the third time today, our physician must hold a meeting with a drugs rep. This man's company has developed a new analogue chlorpromazine antidepressant. Our doctor is not convinced of the benefits to his patients such a drug would bring, so the rep gives him a pair of tickets for both singles finals at this year's Wimbledon Championships.

11. WHEN they graduate from medical school, doctors take the hippocratic oath, a sacred promise that they will help people to the best of their ability. This normally takes the form of ministering to the sick in the community, diagnosing their illnesses and prescribing treatments that will make them better. But they are also happy to help out in other ways too. Here, our doctor is aiding two of his patients by signing their passport applications for £40 a go.

12. ALTHOUGH NHS patients do not pay at source, they are guaranteed the same high quality treatment afforded to the private patient. Here, a little boy comes in complaining of headaches, restricted vision, a tight feeling around his temples and muffled hearing. Using a Computer Aided Diagnostic System, the doctor is able to enter the symptoms into the program, quickly diagnose hemi-facial spasm disorder, and prescribe an extensive course of steroids.

13. ALTHOUGH trained in medicine, it is a fact that the modern doctor will spend a certain amount of his time involved in paperwork. Medical reports have to be written, case notes have to be studied and research literature has to be read to keep up with all the latest developments in drugs and treatments. Here, the doctor finds a brief window in his hectic schedule to write some invoices for his private patients and to sort out his golf club membership.

14. HALFWAY through his afternoon surgery, the doctor has an appointment of his own to keep... at the local golf club. Just as a lorry driver must have a break every so often, a doctor must take a few precious hours two or three times a day to kick back and escape from the demands of his professional life. None of his patients left waiting at the surgery begrudge their GP a little time for himself, and a spot of practice on the putting green is just what the doctor ordered!

15. ON HIS way home, the doctor spots a man who has collapsed with a heart attack. The doctor knows that, tired after a day's work, he could easily make a fatal slip. He therefore decides that it is in the best interests of the man to not volunteer the information that he is a doctor, and crosses the street. In fact, doctors seldom use their professional title, except when booking tables in exclusive restaurants or trying to get their seats upgraded on holiday flights.

LOO ATTENDANT COLUMBO

LAPD HEADQUARTERS.

OH, MY GOD!

WHAT IS IT, ED?

SOMEBODY HAS BLOCKED THE CAN, THEO.

IT'S A REAL MESS IN THERE.

JESUS! LOOK AT ALL THAT BANGERS AND MASH.

I'LL GET THE JANITOR TO SORT IT OUT.

SHORTLY.

LOO ATTENDANT COLUMBO, LAPD GERMICIDE DEPARTMENT...

OH, RIGHT.

WHICH ONE IS IT?

AT THE END THERE.

WAS IT YOU WHO MADE THE DISCOVERY, SIR?

WHAT...? LOOK, CAN'T YOU JUST GET IT CLEANED UP, COLUMBO? IT FUCKIN' STINKS IN HERE.

Out of Order

I CERTAINLY WILL, SIR. YOU CAN BE ASSURED OF THAT. YES INDEED.

TELL ME, HAVE YOU NOTICED ANYBODY WALKING STRANGELY TODAY? SOMEONE WITH A GAIT THAT IS OUT OF THE ORDINARY?

Out of Order

WHAT THE FUCK ARE YOU ON ABOUT?

YOU SEE THE TOP PIECE OF PAPER, SIR? SEE THAT?

THAT'S THE LAST PIECE OF PAPER THAT THE SUSPECT USED...

IT'S STILL DIRTY, AND IT WAS THE FINAL SHEET ON THE ROLL. SO YOU SEE, WHOEVER DID THIS TURD LEFT THIS CUBICLE WITH A CLARTY RINGPIECE.

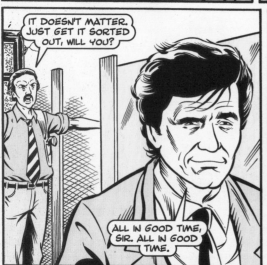

IT DOESN'T MATTER. JUST GET IT SORTED OUT, WILL YOU?

ALL IN GOOD TIME, SIR. ALL IN GOOD TIME.

OH, JUST ONE MORE QUESTION...

WHAT THE FUCK...?

DO YOU EAT A LOT OF FRUIT, SIR?

WHAT? NO. WHY....?

IT'S NOTHING IMPORTANT. I'M JUST CLEARING ONE OR TWO THINGS UP IN MY OWN MIND.

I'M SORRY TO HAVE BOTHERED YOU.

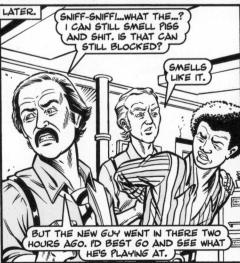

LOOK & LEARN & READ & WONDER

"THE
Mother Nat

FROM THE 13-year-old schoolboy enjoying his first surreptitious drag behind the bikesheds, to the 100-year-old man propped up in bed puffing merrily away, everyone loves a fag. And whether you just have the occasional one after a meal, or you are a dedicated 80-a-day chain smoker, we are all part of one of the world's most finely balanced ecological systems...

1 THE cycle begins at the Cigarette factory, where huge machines labour 24 hours a day, 365 days a year, turning out countless millions of nature's cylindrical wonders, each one a perfect copy of the last. Smiling workers chat happily as they pack the fags neatly into gaily-coloured boxes of 20, before fleets of lorries whisk them away to tobacconists, pubs and off-licences in all four corners of the world.

9 IN AN another amazing 'cycle within a cycle', cigarettes not only bring us TVs, they also bring us the programmes we see on them. Thanks to the generosity of the fag companies, we are able to watch every sport from darts to F1 racing, all free and in the comfort of our own homes.

8 THE tobacco farmer ploughs his land, and sows his seed. The goodness from the smoker is quickly taken up by the young plants, who use it to produce strong healthy leaves, ready to be picked, bundled and sent to the cigarette factory, where the whole wondrous cycle begins again.

6 SADLY, everyone has to die. Our man is now 108 and, though he's never had a day's illness in his life, he has come to the end of his time. Sprinting across the road to buy a paper, he has been hit by a bus. He dies the way he lived, with a smile, and a cigarette, on his lips. But the cycle goes on.

7 ALL the natural goodness of a century's smoking will not go to waste. After the funeral, his body is broken down by micro-organisms, and all the nutrients and minerals from the fags he smoked are returned to the soil from where they came.

92

FAG CYCLE"

e's Miraculous Circle of Life

2 **AN EXCITED** young boy goes into the newsagent for his first cigarette. It's a day he'll remember all his life. Like his parents, and grandparents before him, he proudly hands over a few pennies for 1 Woodbine and a match 'for his father', as he takes his first step on the road to adulthood.

4 **PRETTY** soon, the boy is a man, and cigarettes are his constant companion as he proudly smokes 20, 30, 40 a day. Cigarettes enhance his every waking moment, helping him concentrate, helping him relax. They lead to inner cleanliness, keeping his bowels well toned and regular.

3 **NO PART** of any cigarette is ever wasted. In an amazing 'cycle within a cycle', gentlemen of the road pick the gutters and pavements clean of discarded dog ends, and turn them into... new cigarettes!

5 **OUR** young man has now retired from work, and he can look fondly back at the rewards that half a century of heavy smoking has brought him. Not only a lifetime of pleasure and relaxation, but also more material benefits from the thousands upon thousands of coupons that he has collected over the years.

Next week: *How your body works - an amazing 24 part series.*
Part 1. Your Knackers - Nature's Hairy Glue Factory.

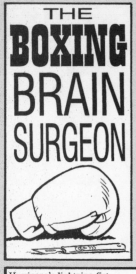

THE BOXING BRAIN SURGEON

There are many strange stories in the world of boxing, but none is more strange, or less true than that of the British heavyweight Billy "Jawbreaker" Hurricane...

This is the most important fight of my career. If I beat Dougie "Dreadnought" Dawson tonight, I'm the heavyweight Champion of Britain...

...but it's the last round and I reckon I'm losing on points. I **have** to knock him out if I'm going to win.

...wait a minute. He's momentarily dropped his guard. I think I can just... yes...

Hurricane's lightning fist found its mark with the force of a baby elephant...

BAM!

UNGERHEURGH!!!

The winner, and the new British Heavyweight Champion, Billy Hurricane!

Few of the blood splattered-crowd could have guessed that the new Champion led a bizarre double life...

...for by day he was a consultant neurosurgeon at the Barndale Infirmary.

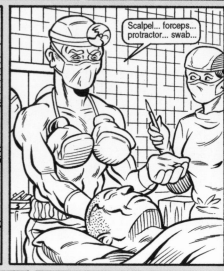

Scalpel... forceps... protractor... swab...

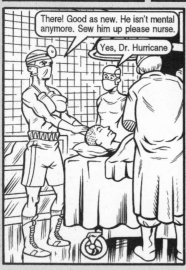

There! Good as new. He isn't mental anymore. Sew him up please nurse.

Yes, Dr. Hurricane

Shortly...

Gosh! Sir Lancelot Robertson-Justice, the Chief Surgeon. I wonder what **he** wants.

Hurricane, old boy!

Good operation, Hurricane. Nice style

Thank you, Sir Lancelot

I think you're ready for a crack at the big one!

This Saturday at four o'clock, there's a really, **really** mental patient coming in...

...do you fancy your chances?

Four o'clock!?...

...I can't!..I...I'm fighting Evander Beauregard for the heavyweight championship of the World this Saturday. The fight starts at half past three.

WHAT!?!

Dammit, man. Is boxing all you ever think about? Now I want you scrubbed up and in this theatre on Saturday at four o'clock.

I'm sorry, Sir Lancelot, I can't!

This is my **one** shot at the title and I can't pass it up. You'll have to get someone else to do it.

There **isn't** anyone else. And I've got **fifty grand** saying you're going to pull this operation off successfully...

...so you're going to **throw that fight**.

But...

I want you to take a dive in the first round and get to that operation. Understand?

Johnny Condor

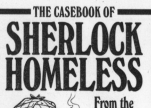

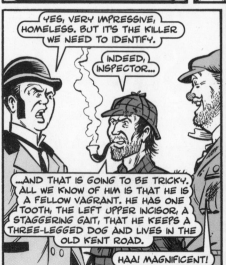

RADIO SHOWS provide the soundtrack to all our lives. Whether it's the commuter driving to work, the brickie working on a building site, or anyone in a situation where its impractical to watch the television, the good old wireless is a friend 24/7. Our favourite DJs and presenters fill the airwaves with their inconsequential chat, keeping us entertained by reading out our requests and dedications. It all seems so slick and professional, but few of us stop to think about the enormous amount of work it takes to put a live radio show together. Let's take a look behind the scenes at a busy broadcasting suite as two very different morning shows hit the national airwaves...

DISC JOCKEY

1 **IN DAYS** gone by, the role of the disc jockey was a simple one - he had to cue up the next disc on his record player whilst announcing the artist and song title. But nowadays the DJ rarely plays records, preferring instead to attempt what amounts to a 3-hour long stand-up comedy routine each morning. This mainly consists of reading out quirky news stories from that day's tabloids, reading out showbiz gossip from that day's tabloids and reading out TV listings from that day's tabloids, all with his own humorous twist. In addition to this, he keeps his listeners entertained by reading out the time, repeatedly saying what day it is and how long it is until the weekend, and reading out inane texts and e-mails from listeners saying how much they love his show. He will also treat his audience to an hilarious catchphase or annoying jingle every fifteen seconds. Desperate for public recognition, the modern DJ looks on his radio show as merely a stepping stone to a television career. If everything goes according to plan, he may perhaps one day rise to the giddy heights of hosting *Celebrity Big Brother's Little Cousin Twice Removed* on More E4+1.

THE POSSE

2 **MODERN** audiences don't want to hear an old-fashioned fuddy-duddy DJ introducing records in a civilised manner. These days the listener expects the presenter's every word to be accompanied by the whoops, cheers and applause of his "posse". In broadcasting circles, this is known as a Zoo Format, so-called because, for the audience, it is like standing in front of a gibbon house whilst being bombarded with faeces. The main function of these talentless professional sycophants is to act as a foil to the presenter, bolstering his ego by screaming with laughter at his every banal utterance. For many twats, being a member of the posse is the first rung on the celebrity ladder. If they play their cards right, they could one day find themselves hosting a 3-minute round-up of lame YouTube clips at 4.00am on the News24 channel, or being lined up to appear on *Celebrity Love Island*. If H out of Steps, Steve Penk and Bob Carolgees drop out at the last minute.

PRODUCER

3 **THE PRESENTER** and his posse may be the anarchic public face of the show, but it is the hard work of the producer that ensures the broadcast runs smoothly. Her first job of the day begins long before the show starts, when she reads through the tabloids and circles the quirky news stories, showbiz gossip and TV listings to be read out. In addition, each week she must sort out the programme's playlist, selecting the few songs that actually make it onto air in the short gaps between the presenter's sidesplitting banter. The station's producers get together and carefully listen to all the new releases for the week. After a long meeting, during which the merits of the various songs are hotly debated, the final playlist is decided according to how much drugs and Russian prostitutes each record company has provided. These chosen few tracks are then put on heavy rotation until the listeners despise them and never want to hear them again.

STUDIO ENGINEER

4 **THE FIRST** rule of radio is that the station must never transmit a moment's silence. A second of "Dead Air", as is is called, can lead to a station's audience going into free-fall as fickle listeners desert in search of the incessant noise they crave. So it falls to the engineer to ensure that his station broadcasts relentless pounding sound with no gaps whatsoever. Because even the best DJ occasionally stops talking for a second, the engineer must be on hand with an endless loop of compressed drum & bass. He also has to ensure that this mindless soundtrack even continues over the news to cover any quiet bits, such as a live feed from Remembrance Day at the Cenotaph, or a report during which the mother of a murder victim becomes speechless with grief at a press conference. He will also have a series of pre-recorded waco noises to play when the DJ is forced to stop talking in order to breathe in. But it's not ju the relentlessness of the noise that's important on radio, it's the volume. The engineer mu monitor his mixer desk throughout the show to ensure that the sound is cranked right up that his meters never drop out of the red.

STUDIO GUEST

5 **EVERY SHOW** must have a guest, and in former times on a music station th might have been a pop singer or band member talking about their latest releas These days however, it's more likely to be an unshaven, second rate stand-up w whom the DJ shares an agent. During the interview, the presenter typically cues up a fe of the comedian's gags, and after a couple of minutes of his routine, asks if he has a DV out. The guest, however, must be careful not to be funnier that his host - a tricky task. If t posse whoop and clap too loudly at his sub-*Mock the Week* material, he may find hims blacklisted and not invited back.

DJ's PR AGENT

6 **AN APPEARANCE** in the newspaper is a great free advert for the radio show, and will help to keep the DJ in the public eye as he pushes for the TV career he so desire Nothing is more certain to get a disc jockey in the papers than listener complain following an off-hand, edgy remark on a controversial subject. It is the PR agent's job carefully word this off-hand, edgy remark for maximum offence, and then orchestrate th ensuing chorus of complaints via a series of sock-puppet e-mail addresses originating fro her agency's offices. This will do wonders for her client's profile and get the producer sacke

RADIO FIRST

07:02

ON AIR

SAY SOMETHING CONTROVERSIAL ABOUT AIDS

Who's Who in a Radio Studio?

PRESENTERS

1 THE TALKLIVE breakfast show has a fast-moving rolling news agenda. The show's topical content is determined by events that are unfolding live, and it is the job of the two presenters to react to changing situations and keep the coverage bang up to date. In these times of digital satellite communications, the presenters could call at a moment's notice upon correspondents around the globe for live reports on any breaking story. However, that takes a lot of organising, so they generally speak to whoever has just been knocked out of *Strictly Come Dancing* the previous Saturday instead. But of course that can't fill three hours every day, so the show also focuses on other aspects of current affairs, such as speculating about who will be knocked out of *Strictly Come Dancing* the following weekend. If there is any time left in the running order, the pair of main presenters fill in by reading out quirky stories from the tabloids, reading out showbiz gossip from the tabloids and reading out TV listings from the tabloids. Like many successful broadcasting partnerships, the secret of their success lies in their on-air chemistry. In this case, the chemistry consists of mutual loathing, jealousy and resentment. Different wages, perceived unfairness over the typesizes used for their respective billings in the *Radio Times*, and the fact that one of them occasionally gets to do a bit of telly all help to fuel a seething, acrid enmity which is quite obvious to even the most casual listener.

TRAVEL ANNOUNCER

2 THE BREAKFAST show goes out at a time when many listeners are driving to work, and regular bulletins from the travel announcer keep these commuters informed of the latest accidents and hold-ups on the roads. A nationwide network of sales reps with bluetooth headsets, van drivers using hand-held phones whilst driving and texting truckers who have taken a 5-minute break from masturbating, send in traffic condition reports. To prevent hoaxes, these are put through a lengthy screening process which ensures that any information is at least two hours out of date by the time it hits the airwaves.

SPORTS REPORTER

3 TALKLIVE is a 24-hour station, and it is the job of the sports reporter to get his busy listeners up to speed on the day's sporting news by providing a potted digest of the main headlines every half hour. His job is to provide his busy listeners with regular, punchy bullet points about the day's important developments from a wide variety of sports, but mainly football. He has direct feeds to his desk from news agencies around the world, as well as a grid of regional footie hacks around the country, although he gets most of his exclusives from the back pages of the *Daily Mirror* and his own team's internet message boards. It is the sports reporter's job to announce the previous day's scores, cover all the transfer news and preview the big matches that are coming up. Unless they're being broadcast on a rival network, in which case they're ignored completely.

CELEBRITY GUEST

4 TALKLIVE breakfast show live interviews are with people who are actually making the news. Politicians, world leaders, sports stars and eminent scientists are all too busy to come to the studio, so guests are usually Z-list celebrities who have just been ejected from whichever reality TV show is currently running. But it's the unexpected mix of opinions that give the programme its fascinating flavour, so it's not just people thrown off *Strictly Come Dancing* who get to appear! Occasionally, people who are still in it are invited to talk about their chances of being ejected the following week. Or sometimes one of the judges might come in and tell listeners who they think is next for the chop.

CALL SCREENER

5 STATIONS like TalkLive give listeners the chance to phone in and air their own opinions on the topics of the day. The vast majority of the public is made up of reasonable, thoughtful people who are capable of calling in and making intelligent contributions on whatever subject is being debated. The call screener's job is to filter out these people, thus allowing a never-ending succession of pig-ignorant taxi drivers from Essex onto the airwaves to spout their bile about Burqas, immigration, health & safety legislation and political correctness gone mad.

NEXT WEEK: Who's Who in a Pole-dancing Club

JACK BLACK AND THE BARBERSHOP MYSTERY

THE JANUARY HOLIDAYS WERE HERE ONCE MORE, AND JACK BLACK AND HIS DOG SILVER WERE STAYING WITH AUNT MEG IN HER DISUSED LIGHT-HOUSE, INJUDICIOUSLY SITUATED IN THE CENTRE OF THE PICTURESQUE BERKSHIRE VILLAGE OF OXTER-ON-THE-LISK.

I'M JUST OFF TO GET MY HAIR CUT, AUNT MEG.

BUT YOU HAD A SHORT BACK AND SIDES LAST WEEK. YOUR HAIR LOOKS LOVELY.

NO. IT'S GETTING TOO LONG. I DON'T WANT TO GET MISTAKEN FOR A COMMUNIST BEATNIK OR SOME SORT OF DEPRAVED HOMOSEXUAL, YOU KNOW.

WELL, DON'T BE BACK LATE. IT'S THE MISS NUDE OXTER-ON-THE-LISK CONTEST AT THE VILLAGE HALL TONIGHT. I WANT YOU AND SILVER THERE TO CHEER ME ON.

GEORGE RANSOME, GENTLEMENS BARBER

AH, JACK. BACK AGAIN?

YES, MR RANSOME. IT'S GETTING A BIT LONG.

GOING ANYWHERE FOR YOUR HOLIDAYS THIS YEAR?

YES. SILVER AND I WILL BE STAYING WITH AUNT MEG IN A VARIETY OF QUIRKY DWELLINGS SITUATED IN MISCELLANEOUS LOCATIONS AROUND THE BRITISH ISLES.

THAT'S NICE...

SUDDENLY...

TING!

EXCUSE ME. I'LL BE BACK IN A MOMENT.

WOW! IT'S BRUCE FORSYTH! I WONDER WHAT HE WANTS?

NICE TO SEE YOU, TO SEE YOU, NICE, MR RANSOME.

MR FORSYTH. I'VE GOT THE...AHEM...MERCHANDISE READY AS USUAL.

HERE IT IS.

DIDN'T YOU DO WELL. E-BIV-VIV-VIV-E-VIB-VE-VIV. GOOD GAME, GOOD GAME.

WHAT WAS ALL THAT ABOUT, MR RANSOME?

SEARCH ME...

...ALL I KNOW IS, BRUCIE COMES IN HERE EVERY WEEK AND BUYS ALL THE HAIR I'VE SWEPT UP OFF THE FLOOR. I'VE NO IDEA WHAT HE DOES WITH IT ALL.

THE STRANGE THING IS, HE NEVER HAS A HAIRCUT HIMSELF.

HOW QUEER.

ANYWAY, THERE WE GO. ALL FINISHED.

SUPER.

ANYTHING FOR THE WEEKEND?

CERTAINLY NOT. MY BALLS HAVEN'T DROPPED YET SO I STILL THINK GIRLS ARE SILLY. COME ON, SILVER. WE DON'T WANT TO BE LATE FOR THE MISS NUDE OXTER-ON-THE-LISK COMPETITION.

OPERATION DESSERT STORM

DATELINE: THE PRESENT DAY. LOCATION: SOMEWHERE IN IRAQ. THE MEMBERS OF THE 88TH BATTALION, THE FULCHESTER LIGHT INFANTRY, SIT DOWN TO A WELL-EARNED MEAL BEFORE ANOTHER DAY IN THE FRONT LINE OF THE WAR AGAINST TERROR.

FIGHTING THE AXIS OF EVIL CERTAINLY GIVES YOU AN APPETITE FOR LUNCH, EH LADS?

NOT 'ARF. THESE PROFITEROLES ARE DELISH!

THEY'RE SO MORE-ISH! YUM! YUM!

WHAT ABOUT SARGE'S CREME BRULEE YESTERDAY. IT WAS TICKETY BOO!

I'LL SAY. TALK ABOUT MELT IN THE MOUTH! IT WAS SCRUMMY.

ANY MORE OF THOSE PROFITEROLES LEFT, SARGE?

AWW!

'FRAID NOT...

...YOU'LL JUST HAVE TO MAKE DO WITH THIS JAM ROLY-POLY INSTEAD, WITH OODLES AND OODLES OF PIPING HOT CUSTARD.

THREE CHEERS FOR SERGEANT CRADDOCK, THE BEST BLOOMIN' PASTRY CHEF IN THE BRITISH ARMY!

HIP! HIP!

HOORAY!

HIP! HIP!

HOORAY!

HIP! HIP!

HOORAY!

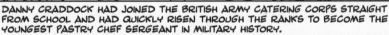

DANNY CRADDOCK HAD JOINED THE BRITISH ARMY CATERING CORPS STRAIGHT FROM SCHOOL AND HAD QUICKLY RISEN THROUGH THE RANKS TO BECOME THE YOUNGEST PASTRY CHEF SERGEANT IN MILITARY HISTORY.

SHORTLY.

WOAH, LOOK AT THE TIME, LADS. COME ON! WE SHOULD HAVE BEEN IN BASRA TEN MINUTES AGO. JOHNNY INSURGENT ISN'T GOING TO GIVE HIMSELF WHAT FOR, IS HE?

'FRAID WE'RE LEAVING YOU WITH THE WASHING UP AGAIN, SARGE.

SEE YOU AT TEA TIME, LADS. KNICKERBOCKER GLORIES AND BANANA SPLITS TODAY.

COR! MY FAVOURITE.

YOUR PUDS ARE BANG ON, SARGE!

BUT LITTLE DID THE MEN OF THE 88TH BATTALION REALISE THAT THE COMPOUND WAS BEING WATCHED...

...BY MULLAH OMAR, ABU HAMZA AND THE MOST WANTED MAN ON EARTH, OSAMA BIN LADEN.

HEH! HEH! THE INFIDELS ARE LEAVING THE CAMP.

EXCELLENT! THE PASTRY CHEF WILL BE ALONE AND UNDEFENDED UNTIL GONE TEA TIME!

THAT LEAVES US PLENTY OF TIME TO PUT OUR EVIL PLAN INTO ACTION.

KRYSTLE'S BIG CHANCE

EVER SINCE SHE WAS A LITTLE GIRL, UGLY KRYSTLE DETROIT HAD DREAMED OF BEING A CHEERLEADER FOR HER LOCAL TEAM, THE ARKANSAS PIGFUCKERS. BUT NATURE HAD PLAYED A CRUEL TRICK ON HER, FOR SHE HAD BEEN CURSED WITH A HIDEOUS DEFORMITY WHICH MEANT SHE WOULD NEVER MAKE THE GRADE.

...AND WHEN I GROW UP, MOM, I'M GONNA BE A CHEERLEADER FOR THE PIGFUCKERS.

GEE, HONEY, IT BREAKS MY HEART TO TELL YOU, BUT YOU'RE NEVER GONNA MAKE IT...

...YOU SEE, TO BE A CHEERLEADER, YOU HAVE TO BE PERFECT IN EVERY WAY. AND I'M AFRAID ONE OF YOUR FRONT TEETH IS OUT OF LINE WITH THE OTHERS...

AND ON YOUR FATHER'S WAGES WORKING AS A LINESMAN FOR THE COUNTY, WE CAN'T AFFORD THE ORTHODONTIST BILL. BUT WE LOVE YOU JUST HOW YOU ARE.

ALTHOUGH SHE KNEW SHE WAS TOO UGLY TO APPEAR IN PUBLIC, KRYSTLE HELPED THE CHEERLEADERS OUT, WORKING LONG HOURS POLISHING BOOTS AND FLUFFING POMPOMS. TODAY WAS THE DAY OF A BIG MATCH AGAINST THEIR ARCH-RIVALS, THE CARBONDALE SASQUATCHES.

HEY, FREAK-FACE! HURRY UP FLUFFING THOSE POMPOMS, WILL YA?

YES, BOBBY-SUE. COMING RIGHT UP.

KRYSTLE STOOD ON THE SIDELINES AS THE GLAMOROUS CHEERLEADERS WENT THROUGH THEIR ROUTINES. SHE HAD WATCHED A THOUSAND TIMES AND KNEW EACH STEP OFF BY HEART.

GIMME A P! GIMME AN I! GIMME A G, F, U!

GIMME A C! GIMME A K! GIMME A E, R, S!

WHAT HAVE YOU GOT?

PIGFUCKERS! WOOO!

SHORTLY.

THAT WAS GREAT, GIRLS. THE BEST I'VE EVER SEEN YOU DO IT.

YEAH! WHATEVER. JUST GET THESE POMPOMS WASHED PRONTO. WE'RE DOING THE PYRAMID AT HALF TIME.

AND JUST MAKE SURE YOU FLUFF 'EM UP GOOD THIS TIME, SNAGGLETOOTH. THE FRONDS ON ONE OF MINE WERE SLIGHTLY FLACCID DURING THE LAST COUPLE OF CONSONANTS.

GEE! I'M SORRY, SHIRLEY-MAY.

AS THE GAME CONTINUED, KRYSTLE WORKED HARD TO GET THE CHEERLEADERS' EQUIPMENT READY IN TIME FOR THEIR NEXT PERFORMANCE.

32, 48, 67, HUT! HUT!

HOT DANG! HE'S GOT A THIRD DOWN AND TEN!

IN a forgotten corner of a Millwall cemetery stands the statue of a young physician holding a pair of aggro boots. Who is he, what is the significance of the boots, and why is he remembered in this forgotten corner. To answer these questions, we must travel back in time to 1889, to the cold and foggy streets of Victorian London.

DOCTOR Martin Boot, a newly qualified chiropodist was late for an important appointment with the Duke of Clarence. "Oh, confound it! The Duke will be furious if I don't deliver his new brothel creepers before nightfall" he cried, and in desperation to make haste, took a short cut through a foggy back alley.

OF a sudden he heard a commotion, and running to investigate, saw a crowd gathered about two men who were brawling. "Great! A fight!" he exclaimed, and quickly joined the excited crowd. The rivals punched and kicked for all they were worth, but all too quickly the fight was over as the loser fell, bloodied and bruised, to the floor.

DOCTOR Boot gently cradled the vanquished man's head in his arms as his life slipped away. "Oh, what a terrible thing to happen" he thought to himself. "I was part of that baying, bloodthirsty crowd. I encouraged this man to fight, and I was enjoying the spectacle. Now, not two minutes later, he lies dead." The doctor hung his head. "Frankly, I feel short changed"

THAT evening in his study, he sat and pondered on the day's events. "The human skull cannot stand prolonged kicking from these old fashioned hobnail boots" he mused. "If only there were a boot as sturdy, but with a more forgiving sole, allowing a fellow to kick someone's fucking head in for longer." There and then, he decided to develop such a boot.

IN his laboratory the next day, Dr. Boot set about his quest to design the footwear that would revolutionise street fighting and take hooliganism into the next century. After a few hours thought, he decided to experiment with the idea of introducing an air pocket into a rubberised sole, thus producing a cushioning effect between boot and head.

WORKING single-mindedly for weeks on end, Dr. Boot experimented with many substances in pursuit of his goal. After countless unsuccessful efforts, he eventually produced a bouncing elastic compound for the sole. Soon afterwards, a prototype slip-on Aggro boot with elasticated sides was ready to be tested.

THE new boot proved to be better than Dr. Boot thought. It passed initial stamping trials on laboratory rats and mice with flying colours. "Excellent. Now to really put it through its paces by kicking this chimpanzee's fucking head in." said the Doctor as he got stuck in to the hapless animal.

BUT disaster struck after only two good wellies to the side of the monkey's face. "Arrrrgh!" Boot yelled, and a sudden searing pain up his calf told him that he had twisted his ankle. Simultaneously, the prototype boot flew from his foot, upsetting a bottle of leeches on the far side of the laboratory.

UNDETERRED by this setback, the Doctor continued his painstaking research over the following months. But with each successive prototype he was beset by the same problem, either he twisted his ankle or the boot came off. The catalogue of failure took its toll on Boot's spirit and he began to despair of achieving his dream.

BUT it's always darkest just before the dawn, and the history of shoes is littered with bizarre coincidence. And Boot's story was to prove no exception. "Do hurry up, Martin dear" said his wife, suddenly entering the study. "We're going to be late for the theatre and I need you to help me do up my Victorian corsets."

AS he pulled on the ropes of his wife's whalebone corset, inspiration struck the doctor like a bolt of lightning. "That's it!. **Corsets**!" he shouted, and suddenly, everything became clear! Slip-on boots were not the answer. "What is needed is a tightly **laced** boot extending half way up the **calf**." he yelled.

LEAVING his bemused wife half corsetted, Dr. Boot fled from the study in a state of great excitement. "I have no time for the theatre, my dear!" he announced. "I intend to work feverishly through the night on a new creation, ignoring all pleas to rest or take food." And with that, he disappeared into his laboratory.

FOR two days and nights the doctor worked like a man possessed in single-minded pursuit of his goal. Eventually, his work complete, he fell exhausted into a deep sleep. He had given all he had to give. He awoke the next day and looked at his new twenty lace hole boot. It was ready to be tested.

DONNING his boot, the doctor set about the chimpanzee in a frenzied attack. "Stitch that you hairy bastard" he screamed as he kicked and he kicked and he kicked. He kicked the chimp's fucking head in for over forty five minutes before it finally lapsed into unconsciousness and died. The new boot was a complete success.

AND so it was that the new 'Patent Botheration Boot' came about and sold in its millions to a fight hungry Victorian public. The history of street brawling and aggravation was to change forever in its wake. But it may all have been very different, had a Victorian lady not entered her husband's study in her corsets.

Shipley's Believe it or Sock!

with the Lord Mayor of Shipley, Alderman Max Weaver

WE ALL LOVE getting socks for Christmas. The mounting thrill of tearing the wrapping paper off a suspiciously soft, sock-sized parcel is the highlight of every man's year. Will they be black, white, brown or grey? Or will they be some other colour? Will they be plain or have all them diamond patterns on them? Or will they have a picture of Homer Simpson on the ankle? Most blokes can't get to sleep on Christmas Eve for the excitement of wondering what sort of socks they're getting the next day!

But where did the custom of giving socks at Christmas come from? What did people give before socks were invented? And what was the most valuable pair of socks ever received? It's time to find out as we answer these and many more fascinating questions about Socks at Christmas...

We all remember the story of the Three Kings from Orient Are who brought gifts of Gold, Frankincense and Myrrh to the baby Jesus in his manger for a bed. But as well as Balthazar, Melchior and Kaspar, the Dead Sea Scrolls refer to a mysterious fourth King from Orient Are. Bathnob arrived at the Bethlehem stable without a gift for the new-born Messiah. Embarrassed, he hurried off to a nearby bazaar, but as it was half-past four on Christmas Eve, all the shops had sold out of good presents and a desperate Bathnob was forced to buy a pair of socks for the infant Christ child. A tradition was born that day which has lasted more than two thousand years.

According to archaeologists, prehistoric societies indulged in their own primitive sock-giving ceremonies to mark the winter solstice. On the shortest day of the year, Neanderthal families would gather at their local henges to give their dads presents. However, weaving technology was still many thousands of years in the future, so stone age socks were not the wool/polyester articles so familiar to us today. Fashioned from animal pelts, primitive Argyll patterns were applied to the skins using burnt sticks and pigments extracted from soil and plants.

In 1622, Queen Elizabeth I sent a Christmas present of a pair of silken socks to her cousin King Philip III of Portugal. Unfortunately the King's mother, Isabella Comptessa of Estoril, was dying of plague and unable to nag her son into writing a thank-you note to the British monarch. This perceived sleight led, in February of 1633, to Elizabeth throwing the Portuguese ambassador into the Tower of London. Philip retaliated by having the British consul to Lisbon executed and displaying his severed head on a spike above the city walls. The London Parliament was recalled, and Prime Minister Oliver Cromwell declared war on the errant Iberian Kingdom. The so-called "War of the Christmas Socks" raged for nearly 24 years and cost an estimated 6,000 lives. To date, it is the largest loss of life ever caused by a single pair of socks.

A rare species of Amazonian ant - the Green Leafcutter - is believed to be the only member of the animal kingdom to give socks at Christmas. The Queen ant secretes a viscous solution of wax and saliva which she uses to coat the feet of the workers in her nest. Scientists believe that this remarkable behaviour is triggered by day-length, occurring as it does on the morning of year's shortest day - coincidentally December 25th. If the Queen runs out of wax and saliva before all the worker ants have been given their "socks", another gland on her abdomen begins to secrete Brut 33 aftershave.

Whilst caught in a blizzard at the South Pole, the members of Captain Scott's ill-fated South Pole expedition decided to keep up morale by exchanging gifts. Because they had no presents with them, the men agreed to exchange socks, parcelling each pair up using blank pages torn from Scott's Journal. According to his diary entry for December 25th 1911, *"...Each member of the party left the tent in turn in order to wrap his socks, so as not to spoil the surprise for the recipient of his gift. I was to exchange with Evans, whilst Bowers and Oates were similarly paired. I was mightily pleased with my gift from Evans, as his socks were in much better condition than my own sorry specimens. However, when Bowers tried on his gift, he was somewhat discomfited to discover that Oates had left several of his toes inside. This occasioned great amusement in the tent, and considerably brightened what would otherwise have been a rather melancholy Christmas Day."*

On Christmas morning 2004, Sir Elton John opened a present from his wife David Furnish to find a pair of diamond-patterned socks. But these were no ordinary socks, for the Argyll patterns on them were made with real diamonds... over 10,000 of them on each sock! The priceless Koh-i-Noor gems used, each one individually sewn onto the socks using 24-carat gold thread and a platinum needle, were said to be have cost Furnish more than £1.2 billion. However, like his idol Frank Sinatra, Elton never wears the same socks twice, and binned the jewel-encrusted pair on Boxing Day.

It is estimated that up to a quarter of Christmas socks end up being inadvertently thrown away when the wrapping paper is cleared up ...that's more than 25 million pairs of unworn socks going into Boxing Day landfill each year. In 1986, inventor Sir Clive Sinclair launched a revolutionary new sock, the Sinclair SX-2000 which, he claimed, would put an end to this problem forever. Costing £399 a pair, each SX-2000 contained an inbuilt computer chip that emitted a loud warning bleep when it sensed itself being put into a binliner full of crumpled wrapping paper. Sinclair's forecast of 10,000,000 sales a week proved unduly optimistic when he failed to sell a single pair, and he was forced to put his company in receivership, close his factory and become a tramp.

In the original version of the 1942 Hollywood musical *Holiday Inn*, Bing Crosby's character Jim Hardy receives a pair of socks from his pal Linda Mason, played by Marjorie Reynolds. Whilst shooting the scene, the notoriously forgetful crooner was unable to remember his lines, and ad-libbed: "They're lovely. I'll have a wank into one of them right now, and save the other one for Boxing Day." Crosby then proceeded to drop his trousers and simulate the performance of a lewd sex act into a sock, whilst singing the song *White Christmas*. The routine reportedly left his fellow cast and crew members helpless with laughter. There followed several days of top level meetings at MGM studios, as producers argued over whether to leave the footage in the final film. However, it was finally decided that masturbation into a sock was too risque for the 1940s US audience, and the scene hit the cutting room floor. In the released version of the movie, Crosby instead sings the song whilst standing by a piano and smoking a pipe.

The astronauts of the Apollo 14 lunar mission found themselves a long way from home on Christmas Day 1971 ... 250,000 miles away to be exact, orbiting the Moon in their space capsule. But NASA boffins had thoughtfully provided them with presents to open on the morning of December 25th - special silver space socks! The socks, woven from a mixture of foil and teflon, had a titanium Argyll pattern on the side and are believed to be the only socks ever made without elastic round the top. That's because, in the gravity-free vacuum of space, socks are just as likely to fall up as down!

NEXT WEEK: GRANGEOVER SAND, THE ONE MAN BAND, GOES BACK TO ANCIENT POMPEII AND STOPS MOUNT VESUVIUS FROM ERUPTING.

The Viz Careers Office

THIS WEEK

So you want to be A BUILDER?

MOST BOYS DREAM of being builders when they grow up, and it's a great career for any lad who is good with his hands. It's a job for life too, because new houses will always need to be built and old houses will always need to be repaired. But what exactly do they do all day? Let's look at the fascinating working life of the modern builder.

▼ **A BUILDER'S** day starts very early in the morning. He goes in his van to pick up his labourers - two heavily-tattoed thugs with convictions for burglary and common assault.

◄ **IT'S OFF** to Acacia Avenue for the first job of the day - repointing Mrs Thompson's garage. Once there, they sit in the cab eating sausage rolls, reading the paper and listening to Radio One for three quarters of an hour. There's just time for a quick cup of tea with six sugars before they drop a bag of cement on the path and drive away, not to return until the following June.

► **IT'S** mid-morning and the builder is pricing up another job, this time to repair some guttering. He gives two quotes - a high one that goes through the books and a much more reasonable one for cash. While the builder surveys the job, his labourers take the opportunity to check the house for window locks and burglar alarms.

▼ **FOR MANY** self-employed tradesmen, cash-flow can often be a problem, and our builder is no exception. Next, he visits a customer to chase up an unpaid £5000 bill for a loft conversion. When the householder complains that he has been waiting eighteen months and the building work hasn't started yet, the builder tells him that if he wants to cancel the job and get a cowboy in to do it, that's up to him, but he will forfeit the £25,000 he has already paid.

▲ **AN HOUR** later, and it's time to get down to some hard graft at last - a spot of plastering. The owner is away, and she has left a key so that they can let themselves in. While the builder helps himself to a cup of tea and a few premium-rate phonecalls, his colleagues indulge in a little good-natured horseplay, rifling through the householder's underwear drawer.

► **IT IS** lunchtime, but work never stops for a busy builder. An angry client calls to remonstrate with him for failing to keep an appointment. The builder tells him that he is very sorry, but his mother has been diagnosed with cancer and he is at that moment giving her a lift to hospital for her chemotherapy treatment. The shocked client apologises and tells the builder to come round only when he feels ready.

▼ **IT'S** Thursday, so after lunch, the builder gives his labourers a lift to the local DSS office where they join the queue and sign on. After that, it's straight back to work.

◄ **OUR** builder prides himself on the quality of his work and he offers a 25-year guarantee. Here, a previous customer has made a complaint about her front door, which she claims the builder has put in upside down and back to front. However, a quick inspection reveals the cause of the problem to be roots from a tree next door growing under the house's foundations and causing the door to turn upside down and back to front.

▶ **HIS NEXT** call-out sees our builder dealing with a problem which is quite common in older houses - rising damp. The wet summer has raised the water table, and the resulting moisture has caused the plaster to weaken and fall off the wall. Before any repair is effected, a damp-proofing course must be installed in the brickwork to ensure that there is no recurrence of the problem. Once again, the householders are out at work and have entrusted the builder with a key.

◄ **LATER ON,** our builders find themselves high up on a roof of a Victorian terrace house where the wind has dislodged some tiles. Genuine Welsh slates are becoming hard to find these days, and prices have risen accordingly. So, in order to maximise profits and make the job easier and quicker, a few slates are prised off the roof of the house next door. This also has the added advantage that the builder can later go round to the neighbour's house and offer to repair their roof, where he has spotted a few missing slates.

▶ **ON THE** way to their next job, the builders spot an attractive woman. British builders have always had an eye for the ladies, and it is refreshing that this quaint and harmless tradition continues, even in these politically correct times. They slow down, and cheekily call out a few good-natured compliments to her.

◄ **HALF-WAY** through the afternoon, and the builders are laying a screed on the conservatory floor of a famous TV magician. Whilst they are waiting for the levelling compound to set, they keep themselves busy looking for pornographic polaroid photographs or home movie footage of the magician's wonderful assistant which they can sell to the News of the World.

▶ **CONSTRUCTION** work invariably creates a lot of rubble and debris, but a good builder always cleans up after himself. Asbestos is very expensive to dispose of properly as it is subject to strict guidelines, so it has to be carefully hidden in the bottom of a skip. Loose aggregate, sand and unused cement, on the other hand, can be safely swept into the drains or flushed down the toilet.

▶ **A BUILDER'S** work is never done, especially if you've paid him up front. Here, the builders leave a half-finished kitchen extension open to the elements to go and finish another kitchen extension which they left open to the elements six months previously, whose owner has taken out a private prosecution. And so another day at the sharp end of the construction industry work is done; eight new jobs started and none finished, five thousand pounds in cash, a dozen bras and several pornographic photographs of a household name in his back pocket.

NEXT WEEK - So you want to be a peepshow wank-booth jizzmopper?

ADVENTURES of JACJAC

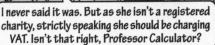

TERROR AT 40,000 FATHOMS

Luxury cruise liner RMS Tupperware Princess is steaming through the freezing waters of the North Atlantic.

In the first class entertainment lounge, her passengers enjoy another evening performance by the ship's resident cabaret star, Tony O'Diamond

...SHA DOOBY-DOOBY DOOO...

...DA DOOBY DOOO!

HOORAY!

HOORAY! MORE!

THANK YOU, LADIES AND GENTLEMEN. ME AND MY TUPPERWARE SERENADERS ARE GOING TO TAKE A SHORT BREAK, BUT WE'LL BE BACK HERE IN ABOUT TWENTY MINUTES...

...TO SING YOU SOME MORE OF YOUR FAVOURITE SONGS.

Mild-mannered sousaphone player Tubby Whitman went to the bar for a drink.

EXCUSE ME...ER...

HELLO THERE. I ENJOYED YOUR PLAYING JUST THEN.

REALLY?

YES. THE SOUSAPHONE IS MY FAVOURITE INSTRUMENT.

G-GOSH! WOULD YOU LIKE A DRINK?

GOOD IDEA. GET ME ONE AS WELL, FATTY, OR WHATEVER YOUR NAME IS. WE'LL BE AT MY TABLE IN THE CORNER.

BUT MR O'DIAMOND...

SUDDENLY...

ALL HANDS ON DECK! LIFE RAFT ON THE STARBOARD BOW!

Everybody rushed out onto the companionway to see what the cause of the commotion was.

HARD ATHWART, BO'SUN! LET'S PICK THOSE MEN UP!

AYE-AYE, CAPTAIN.

Within minutes, the sailors in the life raft were brought aboard.

THANKS FOR RESCUING US, CHAPS. I'M CAPTAIN SANDY BEAUMONT, OF HER MAJESTY'S SUBMARINE HMS PARSIMONIOUS.

I'M CAPTAIN WILLIAMS. WELCOME ABOARD THE TUPPERWARE PRINCESS. BUT WHAT HAPPENED TO YOU? WHERE'S YOUR SUB?

I'M AFRAID IT'S BEEN HIJACKED...

HIJACKED!?!

...BY OSAMA BIN LADEN AND ABU HAMZA!

WHAT!? BUT WHY? WHAT WOULD AL QUAEDA WANT WITH A NUCLEAR SUBMARINE?

THEY'VE GOT A DASTARDLY PLAN.

THEY'RE GOING TO USE IT TO VOYAGE TO THE BOTTOM OF THE SEA....AND PLANT A BOMB ON THE WRECK OF THE TITANIC!

GREAT SCOTT! THE FIENDS!

Meanwhile, 20,000 leagues beneath the surface.

THERE SHE IS, ABU! THE TITANIC! ALI BONGO BE PRAISED!

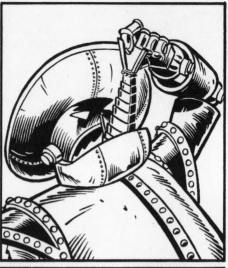

TOPLESS Skateboard Nun

One day, Sister Mary and her Mother Superior were taking a quiet stroll in the country.

WHAT A BEAUTIFUL DAY IT IS, SISTER MARY.

Suddenly...

QUICK, THE DAM. IT'S CRACKING.

The two nuns went to investigate.

OH NO! THE SCHOOL BUS. IT'S BROKEN DOWN ON THE DAM. ALL THOSE CHILDREN ARE IN DANGER.

IF ONLY WE COULD HELP. ALL WE CAN DO IS PRAY FOR THEM.

But Sister Mary knew exactly what she must do...

And in seconds, she had transformed herself into...

...Topless Skateboard Nun!

In a flash she had skated across the crumbling dam to the stricken bus...

COR, JESUS!

QUICK. THERE'S NO TIME TO EXPLAIN. FOLLOW ME.

The children were soon being led to safety.

MICHAEL ROW THE BOAT ASHORE HALLELOOOOOO YAH

A few hours later, the dam gave way.

Shortly...

THANK YOU, TOPLESS SKATEBOARD NUN, WHOEVER YOU ARE. YOU SAVED THOSE CHILDREN'S LIVES.

BLESS YOU, MY SON.

WA-HAY. DOWN BOY.

NEXT WEEK – *Nymphomaniac Pogo-Stick Nurse.*

WILLIAM SHAKESPEARE'S MODEL THEATRE

IT IS 1569, AND CLOUDS OF FOMENT GATHER OVER THE FIELDS OF ENGLAND. UNMARRIED, QUEEN ELIZABETH I HAS NO OBVIOUS HEIR AND MANY PRETENDERS JOSTLE FOR POWER IN THE LENGTHENING SHADOWS BEHIND THE THRONE.

ONE GROUP OF PLOTTERS, LED BY THOMAS PERCY, EARL OF NORTHUMBERLAND, IS DETERMINED TO WRESTLE THE CROWN FROM ELIZABETH'S GRASP AND SETTLE IT UPON THE CATHOLIC HEAD OF HER COUSIN, MARY, QUEEN OF SCOTS.

BUT SUCH MACHINATIONS ARE FAR FROM THE MINDS OF THE EXCITED PEOPLE OF STRATFORD UPON AVON. IT IS CHRISTMAS EVE, AND THE WHOLE TOWN IS PREPARING FOR A ROYAL VISIT THE VERY NEXT DAY.

PLAN of STRATFORD On Avon

RIVER AVON

GADZOOKS. ISN'T IT EXCITING. HER MAJESTY COMING HERE TO STRATFORD UPON AVON.

FRESH FRUIT

GAWD BLESSAH!

MEAT

WELCOME QUEEN ELIZABETH YE FIRST

SHE'S MARVELLOUS, ISN'T SHE?

YES. SHE ALWAYS HATH A SMILE FOR EVERYONE.

WILLIAM! WILLIAM! WHEREFORE ART THOU?

YE NEWE TEA SHOPPE
Prop. J. Shakespeare

HITHER, FATHER. I'M DOING A PLAY IN MY TOY THEATRE.

IT'S ALL ABOUT A DANISH PRINCE WHO IS TRYING TO TAKE REVENGE FOR HIS FATHER'S MURDER AND PURGE THE COURT.

I'M NOT INTERESTED, WILLIAM.

THERE ARE CUSTOMERS WAITING TO BE SERVED.

THOSE THREE OVER THERE, FOR INSTANCE. VERILY, GO AND SEE WHAT THEY WANT.

OKAY, FATHER.

WHAT CAN I GET YOU, GENTLEMEN?

THREE TEAS, BOY. AND SOME SCONES.

AND BE QUICK ABOUT IT, OR I'LL KICK YOUR BACKSIDE FOR YOU.

WELL SAID, NORFOLK.

I DOUBT WE'LL SEE THOSE TEAS THIS SIDE OF ST. STEPHEN'S DAY. METHINKS THE BOY'S ONE DOUBLET SHORT OF A HOSE.

AYE! VERILY HE IS A SIMPLETON RIGHT ENOUGH.

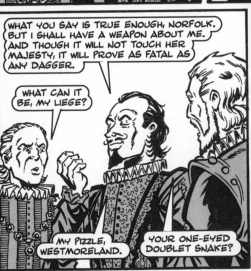

I CAN'T JUST STAND BY AND LET THE QUEEN BE MURDERED MOST FOUL. I SHALL HAVE TO ACT. BUT HOW?

IN THE EARLY HOURS OF CHRISTMAS MORNING, YOUNG WILLIAM SHAKESPEARE AND HIS DOG SILVIO SLIPPED OUT INTO THE FROZEN STREETS OF STRATFORD UPON AVON...

...AND IN THROUGH THE WINDOW OF NORTHUMBERLAND'S ROOM AT THE SWAN INN.

LATER THAT DAY.

IT GIVETH ME GREAT PLEASURE TO DECLARETH THIS NEW BLACK DEATH WING WELL AND TRULY...

STOP!

LORD PERCY?

THE VERY SAME. AND THEY DON'T CALL ME LORD PERCY FOR NOTHING!

WHAT DO YOU RECKON TO THIS!

NORTHUMBERLAND! NO!

HAAA! HA! HA!

HAAA! LOOK AT IT! IT LOOKS LIKE AN ACORN!

VERILY. ONLY SMALLER!

BUT...I DON'T UNDERSTAND...

GUARDS! SEIZE HIM!

WOULD SOMEBODY TELL ME WHAT'S GOING ON?

HE! HE!...I FEAR LORD PERCY WAS INVOLVED IN POPISH PLOT ON YOUR LIFE.

WHAT!?! BUT HOW? HE ONLY FLASHED HIS MANHOOD AT ME.

YES, YOUR MAJESTY. BUT LORD PERCY IS FAMED THROUGHOUT THE LAND FOR HIS MONSTROUS PILLICOCK. WOMEN OF ILL REPUTE HAVE BEEN KNOWN TO FAINT JUST LOOKING AT IT. SHOULD YOUR MAJESTY'S GAZE HAVE FALLEN UPON IT IN ITS FULL GLORY, OR EVEN JUST HALF A TEA CAKE, THE SHOCK WOULD HAVE SENT YOU TO YOUR MAKER.

BAH! WE ARE UNDONE, NORTHUMBERLAND. THANKS TO YOUR HORN OF PLENTY SHRIVELLING UP LIKE A MOUSE'S CONCERTINA.

I DON'T UNDERSTAND IT. IT'S NEVER HAPPENED TO ME BEFORE.

PERHAPS I CAN EXPLAIN...

...USING THE MEDIUM OF THEATRE.

OUR STORY BEGINS IN A STRATFORD UPON AVON TEA SHOP. ENTER STAGE LEFT THREE PLOTTERS, NORTHUMBERLAND, NORFOLK AND WESTMORLAND, ON REGICIDE BENT.

WILLIAM WENT ON TO EXPLAIN HOW IN THE EARLY HOURS OF THE MORNING HE HAD CREPT FROM HIS BED TO THE PLOTTER'S INN. ONCE THERE HE HAD STOLEN INTO NORTHUMBERLAND'S ROOM AND FILLED THE WOULD-BE ASSASSIN'S COD PIECE WITH SNOW AND ICE. AND IT WAS THIS FREEZING SNOW THAT CAUSED HIS TACKLE TO SHRINK TO SUCH COMICAL PROPORTIONS.

OUR PLAY IS DONE AND I WOULDST FAIN, 'TWAS SNOW THAT SAVED, THE GOOD QUEEN'S REIGN.

WENT ON A BIT, DIDN'T IT?

MY LEGS HAVE GONE TO SLEEP.

BRAVO, MASTER SHAKESPEARE.

THAT WAS A VERY GOOD PLAY, YOUNG MASTER SHAKESPEARE, THOUGH THE JOKES WERE A BIT SHIT AND I DIDN'T UNDERSTAND WHAT WAS GOING ON HALF OF THE TIME. STILL PEOPLE MIGHT LIKE IT IN 400 YEARS TIME.

THANK YOU, YOUR MAJESTY.

NEVERTHELESS, YOU HAVE SAVED THE KINGDOM, AND AS SUCH YOU DESERVE A REWARD.

ZOUNDS!

AND AT FIVE O'CLOCK.

THERE YOU ARE, WILLIAM. A PROPER THEATRE OF YOUR OWN, COMPLETE WITH A COMPANY OF NEUROTIC ACTORS. NOW YOU CAN PUT ON ALL THE PLAYS YOU WANT.

WOW! THANKS, YOUR MAJESTY. THAT'S THE BEST CHRISTMAS PRESENT EVER!

THE ROYAL SHAKESPEARE THEATRE

The Stock Ex

TO MANY OF US, the workings of the stock exchange are a complete mystery. It may look as though the floor is full of men just waving bits of paper and shouting. But in fact they are keeping the wheels of Britain's economic machine turning. And like most machines, it's really very simple to understand once you know what the key components are and what they do...

1 THIS man is a *Trader*. He holds up and waves small pieces of paper and shouts numbers to his colleague. If he shouts the wrong numbers or if his colleague mishears him, millions of pounds could be wiped off share values across the world.

2 THE *Electronic Display* is the nerve centre of the whole stock exchange. From the minute the exchange opens to the ceasing of trading in the evening, very important numbers to many, many decimal places scroll across its screen, far too fast for anyone to read. It is the task of the underwriter to point excitedly at some of these numbers, and scream selected ones into a phone.

3 THE *Futures Trader* sits in an air conditioned office up in the gantry. He compares the figures shouted at him by the Underwriter with some others on his computer screen. He has to make split second decisions whether to buy these numbers or sell them. A wrong decision could cost him a million pounds.

6 THIS is a *Bull*. He has just spent four billion pounds that he doesn't have, and that doesn't exist, buying something which also doesn't exist, from a man who doesn't own it. The deal done, the imaginary thing is immediately sold back to the Bull, who uses the original nonexistent money to pay for it. Thanks to the magic of the Stock Exchange, both men have just made a million pounds.

7 THIS is a *Stag*. He buys things that don't exist, but using money that does, but which he doesn't own. He then sells them on to himself, and the money therefore becomes his.

8 THIS is a *Bea* This is a hug carnivorou mammal of the genus *Ursus*. has escape from the zoo.

10 THE *Broker* is a very skilled man, for it his job to go redder in the face than anyone else on the Stock Exchange floor. Not only that, but he must constantly wave bits of paper and attempt to jostle to the front of a crowd of screaming Jobbers gathered around somebody on a small platform called the *Jobbers' Stand*.

9056 9056 9056 9056 9056 9056 9056
9055 ...55 9055 A 9055 9055 9055 9055
9043 9043 9043 9043 9043 9043
9041 9041 9041 B 9041 9041 9041 9041

change

4 THIS man is not an actual trader, but has simply entered the Stock Exchange looking for his son, who has forgotten his sandwiches. He sees him across the floor and, attempts to attract his attention by waving and shouting. In doing so, he inadvertently makes himself a million pounds, and causes 200 brokers in Tokyo to jump to their deaths from a skyscraper.

5 IT is the job of the *Speculator* to shout some numbers into one of four telephones he is holding. At the same time, his colleague is scribbling things onto little bits of paper and giving them to other members of the stock exchange. They are handed from one to another before finally being thrown on the floor.

9 THE men in the stripy blazers, shouting frantically are the *Jobbers*. It is their job to shout frantically in stripy blazers. A good Jobber, if he shouts loud enough and if his blazer is stripy enough, can earn an annual bonus of £2m.

137

Special Brew
Through the Ages

THE ANCIENT Egyptians worshipped Special Brew, believing it to have supernatural properties. When Howard Carter broke into the tomb of Amenhotep and ransacked his sarcophagus, he found the boy king buried along with all his possession

NO-ONE knows exactly when Special Brew was discovered, but archaeologists believe that its miraculous qualities were well known to man over 4 million years ago. Primitive paintings found in caves in Denmark suggest that Bronze Age artists were rgularly ripped to their hairy tits on Special Brew.

THE LADY of Lamp - Floren Nightingale - saved countless lives duri the Crimean War. A token of his gratitu the Prime Minister Gladstone awarde her a lifetime's sup

ENGLISH history would have taken a very different course had it not been for Special Brew. On November 5th 1066, Guy Fawkes and his fellow conspirators crept into the cellars of the Houses of Parliament, intending to blow up King James I with some fireworks. However, they discovered a pallet of Special Brew and stopped for refreshment. After four tins each, they decided that the King was actually a smashing bloke, and their best mate, and the plot was off.

THE ROMANS recognised Special Brew's fight-starting properties and put it to good use in the Colosseum. Gladiators would be plied with 'Spesh' before a battle to ensure they put on a good show for the bloodthirsty crowd. After a fight, the surviving gladiators would sacrifice a goat to Trampicus, the Roman god of unusual mental states.

Spesh' and granted her the keys to
de Park so as she could have a well-
served sit-down. Over the next 50
rs, she became a well known figure,
ertaining children with her colourful
guage, explicit language and frequent
uts of vomiting.

The story of the glorious drink that has forged civilisations

AND SO to the present day, where this remarkable drink, with its unequalled capacity to make your head go funny, is still enjoyed by everyone. From Her Majesty the Queen right down to the lowliest tramp, all agree that there is only one way to start the day. And that's by shotgunning a couple of tins of Special Brew -
the drink that's made history!

Jack Black & his dog Silver in

The Case of the MYSTERIOUS PLUMBER

THE SHORTLY-AFTER-CHRISTMAS HOLIDAYS WERE HERE AGAIN, AND JACK BLACK AND HIS DOG SILVER WERE STAYING WITH AUNT MEG IN HER TUDOR COTTAGE IN THE NORFOLK VILLAGE OF RICHMAL-ON-THE-CROMPTON.

J. CHURCHILL PLUMBER
RICHMAL 326
J. CHURCHILL PLUMBER
RICHMAL 326
NO JOB TOO SMALL

HELLO, JACK. DID YOU HAVE A NICE WALK?

I'LL SAY, AUNT MEG. WE FOUND AN OSPREY NEST ON THE MOORS AND WE SMASHED THE EGGS, AND SILVER CHASED SOME COUNCIL ESTATE CHILDREN WHO WERE HAVING A PICNIC.

GOSH!

HOW WAS YOUR DAY?

TERRIBLE. I'VE HAD TO DO ALL THE LAUNDRY BY HAND AGAIN.

THE WASHING MACHINE STILL BROKEN, IS IT?

YES, BUT NOT FOR MUCH LONGER, JACK. THE PLUMBER IS FIXING IT AS WE SPEAK.

JACK, THIS IS JANE CHURCHILL, THE PLUMBER.

HI, JACK. NICE TO MEET YOU.

EH!?!

ALL DONE, MEG. GOOD AS NEW. IT WAS JUST A WASHER ON THE INLET HOSE THAT HAD PERISHED. I'VE REPLACED IT AND PUT AN IN-LINE TAP IN THE PIPE SO YOU DON'T HAVE TO SHUT OFF THE WHOLE SUPPLY NEXT TIME. I'LL SEND MY BILL OVER.

THANK YOU, JANE. BYE.

WHAT ARE YOU THINKING OF? LETTING A LADY PLUMBER LOOSE ON YOUR PIPES!

I HAVEN'T ANY CHOICE. SHE'S THE ONLY PLUMBER IN THE VILLAGE SINCE OLD MR MOSSCROP DROWNED IN THE CANAL.

HMM! I SUPPOSE.

WAIT A MINUTE. YOU'RE NOT SERIOUSLY THINKING OF USING THAT MACHINE, ARE YOU?

WHY EVER NOT? IT'S BEEN FIXED, HASN'T IT?

WELL, POSSIBLY, BUT THERE IS NO WAY I'M GOING TO LET YOU TURN THAT THING ON UNTIL IT'S BEEN CHECKED...

...BY A MAN.

IS THAT MR JOHNSON? HELLO, IT'S JACK BLACK FROM NEXT DOOR. I WONDER IF YOU COULD POP ROUND AND CHECK SOME PLUMBING THAT AUNT MEG HAS HAD DONE. THIS AFTERNOON? THAT'S GREAT, THANK YOU.

WHAT'S WRONG, AUNT MEG?

HALF MY UNDERWEAR HAS GONE.

GONE!?! WHERE?

I DON'T KNOW.

IVORY SNOW

ORDINARILY I'D HAVE ACCUSED THE PLUMBER, AS THEY ALWAYS STEAL WOMEN'S LINGERIE FOR...WELL...FOR ALL SORTS OF MUCKY NONSENSE.

YOU MEAN...

YES, JACK. SNIFFING AND WANKING.

EURGH! THE BEASTS!

BUT THE ONLY TRADESMAN WHO'S BEEN IN THE HOUSE TODAY IS JANE, AND SHE WAS A WOMAN.

HMM! IT DOESN'T MAKE SENSE.

OH WELL. LUCKILY, THERE'S A NEW SECOND HAND LADIES' UNDERWEAR SHOP OPENED IN THE VILLAGE. POP DOWN AND BUY ME A DOZEN PAIRS OF ASSORTED FRILLIES, WOULD YOU?

CERTAINLY, AUNT MEG.

COME ON, SILVER.

JACK AND SILVER MADE THEIR WAY TO THE VILLAGE.

UNMENTIONABLES

PROP: EVADNE TILLOTSON

PRE-OWNED FEMININE NETHERGARMENTRY.

NEW STOCK DAILY.

GOOD MORNING, MRS TILLOTSON. COULD I HAVE A DOZEN PAIRS OF LADIES WOTNOTS, PLEASE?

OF COURSE. ARE THEY FOR YOU, YOUNG MAN?

PICK 'N' MIX KNICKS

CERTAINLY NOT! WHAT WOULD I WANT WITH THEM?

OH, YOU KNOW. ALL THAT ADOLESCENT NONSENSE AND CARRY ON THAT YOU YOUNG BOYS GET UP TO.

HOW DARE YOU! THEY'RE FOR MY AUNT MEG.

GRRRR!

WHAT IS IT, BOY? WHAT HAVE YOU FOUND?

STAFF ONLY

A WRENCH!?! WHAT ON EARTH IS THAT DOING HERE? THIS IS ALL GETTING VERY SUSPICIOUS.

AS HE WALKED BACK TO MEG'S COTTAGE, THE JUNIOR GUMSHOE'S MIND WAS WHIRLING. WHY HAD AUNT MEG'S UNDIES DISAPPEARED DURING THE PLUMBER'S VISIT? WHERE WAS THE SECOND HAND UNDERWEAR SHOP GETTING ITS STOCK FROM? AND WHY WAS THERE A PIPE WRENCH IN AMONGST THE KNICKERS?

NONE OF THIS MAKES SENSE, SILVER.

AH, JACK. MR JOHNSON IS LOOKING AT THE WASHING MACHINE FOR ME.

GREAT! I DARE SAY THAT SO-CALLED PLUMBER HAS MADE A RIGHT BOTCH OF IT.

OH!?!

ACTUALLY, JACK, NO...

I MEAN I'M NOT A PLUMBER, I'M A CALLIGRAPHER BY TRADE. BUT IT LOOKS LIKE A PRETTY DECENT JOB TO ME...

BUT YOU DID RIGHT TO CALL ME. YOU CAN'T BE TOO CAREFUL. I ONCE HAD A LADY ELECTRICIAN ROUND TO CHANGE A BULB FOR ME. THE FIRST TIME I TURNED IT ON THE TELEVISION EXPLODED, THE FUSE BOX MELTED AND ALL THE LIGHTS IN THE VILLAGE WERE OFF FOR A WEEK.

BUT YOU'RE SAFE TO TURN YOUR WASHING MACHINE ON, MEG. THAT JOB IS AS GOOD AS ANY MAN COULD HAVE DONE.

I WONDER...

SILVER, IT'S TIME WE SORTED OUT THIS MYSTERY ONCE AND FOR ALL.

WOOF!

...AND I THINK I KNOW JUST HOW TO DO IT.

THE NEXT DAY.

GOOD MORNING, JANE. THANKS FOR COMING SO QUICKLY.

THAT'S OKAY, MEG. WHAT SEEMS TO BE THE PROBLEM?

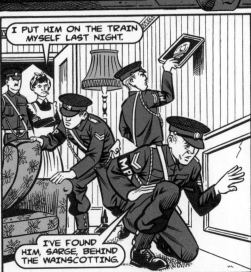

FINALLY, AFTER A THREE MONTH JOURNEY IN A WARDROBE ACROSS OCCUPIED EUROPE, NUGENT ARRIVED AT THE WAR OFFICE IN WHITEHALL.

WAR OFFICE

BEEP!

AND...

THUMP!

WHAT THE DEVIL!?!

NEVER...IN THE FIELD OF HUMAN CONFLICT...HAS A MEETING BEEN SO DISRUPTED!

KNOCK! KNOCK! KNOCK! KNOCK! KNOCK! KNOCK!

COME OUT! COME OUT OF THAT WARDROBE AT ONCE, DO YOU HEAR ME?

SERGEANT! GET HIM OUT!

PERCY 'HIDER' NUGENT! I MIGHT HAVE GUESSED! WELL, YOU'VE HIDDEN FOR THE LAST TIME, LET ME TELL YOU!

BUT, SIR! TAKE A LOOK AT THIS!

GOOD GRIEF!

WHAT IS IT, BRIGADIER?

IT'S ADOLF HITLER'S TOP SECRET PLANS.

DATES, TIMES, CODE WORDS - THE LOT!

WHY, WITH THIS INFORMATION IN OUR HANDS, WE CAN HAVE THE WAR WON IN A MATTER OF DAYS, PRIME MINISTER!

I'LL JUST GO BACK IN HERE, IF YOU DON'T MIND, GIVE ME A SHOUT WHEN IT'S ALL OVER.

OH NO YOU DON'T, NUGENT. YOU'VE BEEN AWOL FOR THREE MONTHS.

LEAVE HIM, MAJOR. THIS GLORIOUS NATION OF OURS...

...THIS SCEPTERED ISLE, OWES PRIVATE NUGENT A GREAT DEAL OF GRATITUDE...

...LEAVE HIM IN THE WARDROBE, AND LET US WASTE NO MORE TIME IN PUTTING A STOP TO HERR HITLER'S PLANS.

AND SO IT WAS, THAT JUST TWO DAYS AFTER NUGENT'S DELIVERY OF THE GERMAN PLANS TO WHITEHALL, HITLER AND HIS NAZI WAR MACHINE CRUMBLED LIKE THE PUTRID, EVIL SCUM DOGS THAT THEY WERE.

EXTRA! EXTRA! READ ALL ABOUT IT!

WAR OVER AND WE'VE WON!

THANKS TO PERCY 'HIDER' NUGENT, THE WAR WAS CUT MERCIFULLY SHORT. PERCY CAME OUT OF THE WARDROBE THE DAY THE WAR ENDED AND WENT HOME, WHERE HE CONTINUED TO HIDE INTERMITTENTLY FOR THE REST OF HIS LIFE. HE HID IN A SHED ON HIS FRIEND'S ALLOTMENT DURING THE ACTION IN KOREA AND SPENT THREE MONTHS UNDER THE FLOORBOARDS AT HIS SISTER'S HOUSE THROUGHOUT THE FALKLANDS CONFLICT. NUGENT DIED PEACEFULLY UNDERNEATH HIS BED IN 1993, AT THE RIPE OLD AGE OF 72. ON HIS DEATH, A FUND WAS STARTED IN HIS MEMORY AND ENOUGH MONEY WAS RAISED TO ERECT A BRONZE STATUE OF HIM WHICH STANDS TO THIS DAY, HIDING BEHIND THE CURTAINS IN THE WAR OFFICE AT WHITEHALL.

Who's who at a Professional Foo

A behind-the-scenes look at who does what,

all Club
nd off the field

1 Manager
The manager is the head of the team. A purple-faced, shifty-eyed alcoholic, he assesses the abilities of his squad, selecting the best eleven men for each game. A tactical mastermind, he works out a specific team strategy for each match, before spending every Saturday afternoon standing on the touchline screaming four letter abuse at his players. After the match, win or lose, he must give an interview to the press using vocabulary just beyond his intellectual grasp. His most important function is to get sacked by the chairman when the team loses three matches in a row. He is then free to spend his bung-money on a string of high-class racehorses and whores.

2 Assistant Manager
Easily identifiable by the tracksuit that he wears 24 hours a day, he must stand slightly behind and to one side of the manager during training sessions, repeating what the manager says and pointing in the same direction. The assistant manager is the manager's drinking and gambling partner and he is appointed and sacked along with him. Even less articulate than the manager, he is nevertheless occasionally called on to paper over the cracks at press conferences when the manager is too busy receiving bungs at motorway service stations or has fallen asleep under a hedge.

3 Captain
The manager's pet, and usually the player with the shortest criminal record. He is often called upon to speak to the press as he is the least inarticulate of the team, capable of stringing two or even three cliches together in the same sentence. As the ambassador for the club, he takes his responsibilities seriously, letting off only a few fire extinguishers in foreign hotels. He is usually appointed caretaker player-manager five games from the end of the season when the chairman pisses off and the manager's liver has gone.

4 Star Striker
A mercurial talent, he initiates all the attacks, both on the field and in the nightclub. His behaviour is constantly excused by the manager on the grounds that he is "young and inexperienced and under a lot of pressure". What he means is that he is too good a player to tell to fuck off.

5 Luxury Player
The player that causes the manager the most problems. He must be played enough to maintain his reputation and his value, but not too often as his legs are prone to snap like dry twigs. Fortunately for the manager, he is usually suspended, in a drug rehabilitation centre, or in court charged with beating his girlfriend up.

6 Chairman
A fat crook, usually with his own highly dodgy business. He takes credit for good results and blames the manager for bad ones. It is the chairman's job to use a tiny fraction of his vast personal fortune to bankroll the club. He must also ensure that the fans are shafted as deeply and as comprehensively as possible as quickly as possible. The moment the club's fortunes begin to dip, he has to piss off with his pockets full of cash.

7 Chairman's 2nd Wife
She is the younger and better-looking wife that the chairman took on after accruing his fortune. She plays an important role on match days by providing pre-game footage for Match of the Day. During the match itself, she looks dolefully around in every direction except where the ball is. She stays at her husband's side all the time making sure he has a constant supply of fatty foods and high-tar cigarettes.

8 Celebrity Supporter
A fanatical follower of the team ever since his television career started to nosedive, he turns out rain or shine to all televised home matches. Honoured by fellow supporters with his own songs - '(Insert name of Celebrity supporter), is a wanker, is a wanker' and 'Who the fucking hell are you?'

9 The Mascot
The club's spirit personified. He keeps morale high before the game by dressing up as an animal with enormous shoes, falling over and giving the crowd something to aim pies and coins at.

10 Physiotherapist
A short, fat man who defies nature by being able to sprint faster than a cheetah over 80 yards whilst keeping the upper half of his body and the bag he carries perfectly still. His main responsibilities are to provide instant first-aid to injured players, and to develop physical characteristics which cause amusement to opposing fans.

11 Temperamental Homesick Brazilian
A World Cup hero signed in a fanfare of publicity to the delight of hopeful fans. The whole town erupts in a carnival fever of hastily-bought wigs, marraccas, mariachi drums and whistles. Twenty minutes later, he's back on the plane home, cursing his adoptive town as a freezing petrochemical shit-hole.

12 Substitute Winger
Passes on valuable international experience to younger players, like how to lose £4 million on a Portuguese hotel complex and still have to play at 38, despite two decades of top-flight football.

13 Ex-star Player
Always in demand on local radio, where he can be relied upon to bad-mouth the club, explaining to anyone who will listen how this team isn't a patch on the one he used to play in. He serves a valuable purpose by keeping alive expressions like 'centre half', 'pearler' and 'banana shot'. Often to be seen giving TV interviews outside the ground - from which he is periodically banned.

14 The trainee
The young seventeen-year-old football genius who is the future of the club. He possesses the dazzling qualities of skill and speed allied with fitness and enthusiasm. His job is to sit on the bench while the supporters sing his name, and to be sold in a relegation year for buttons, before enjoying a sparkling international career with Manchester United.

15 The Talent Scout
The only member of the club's staff who knows anything about football, he could - if he was ever called upon (which he never will be) - make a much better job of running the club than the manager. He's supported the club all his life, he discovered every talented player the club ever sold, the Chairman doesn't know him from Adam, and he has to buy his own away tickets.

16 The Club Sponsor
The man who spends his staff's Christmas bonuses printing his company logo on the team's shirts, in return for two season tickets and the Celebrity Supporter's phone number.

17 The Star Striker's Girlfriend
A lightweight TV presenter, she is presently shagging her way through all the Star Strikers in the division. She is often to be seen flashing her spider's legs in lad-mags, or stifling a yawn in the Directors' Box, whilst staring vacantly in the same direction as the Chairman's Second Wife.

18 The Substitute Defender
The club donkey - who makes up for his workaday abilities with a surfeit of aggression. Called upon by the manager to take the field when the opposing team fields a player of such talent that he needs to be hospitalised.

19 The "Club Insider"
It is his job to undermine all secret multi-million pound transfer negotiations at the club. In return, he gets free drinks two nights a week down the pub with the local newspaper's Sports reporter.

More READ & LEARN next week.

This Week: The Breville Sandwich Toaster

The backs of our kitchen cupboards are an Aladdin's cave of half-arsed inventions. From the dusty Sodastream to the rusting 9-in-1 Veg-O-Matic slicer, this is where we abandon our kitchen inventions after using them a couple of times.

1. IN EACH of our homes this graveyard of culinary novelties stands as a dust-covered testament to our boundless optimism and our touching belief in the face of experience that the latest £14.99 problem-solving device will change our lives forever.

2. THE STORY of the sandwich toaster begins in turn of the century Austria. Doctor Ernst Breville, a young scientist from Belgrade's K-Tel Institute of Tupenny Ha'penny Engineering, was attending a convention of not very good inventors at the prestigious University of Vienna.

3. HE ATTENDED a demonstration of Professor Ulrich Ronco's revolutionary Buttoneer - a handheld device using bright red plastic rivets to attach buttons in exactly twice the time it takes to sew them on. There was great excitement amongst the third-rate inventors in the lecture theatre.

4. THE BUTTONEER was the toast of the conference and Breville attended a reception to celebrate its successful unveiling. He found himself so deep in conversation with Professor Ronco that there was no time to eat. Putting a cheese sandwich in his back pocket he resolved to eat it later at his hotel.

5. BACK IN his room that night, Breville's mind was in a spin. "If only I had the lacklustre vision of Professor Ronco. Why can't I invent something as negligibly useful as the Buttoneer?" he thought, as he folded his breeches into the Corby trouser press.

6. HE RETIRED to bed, but five minutes later he noticed a strong smell of burning cheese. At first he thought it must be the nearby hotel kitchens, but then the realisation dawned on him. "Oh no!" he cried. "I forgot about the sandwich in my pocket!"

7. BREVILLE rescued his trousers only to discover that the press had toasted the sandwich. The bread was brittle and the filling as hot as molten lava. Not only that, but the trouser press was encrusted with burnt cheese and scorched butter. Breville's keen inventor's mind began to race.

8. "WHAT IF I could develop a machine that toasted sandwiches too hot to eat, whilst leaving itself impossible to clean properly afterwards?" he mused. "Everybody would buy one and use it once or twice!" He resolved to return to Belgrade the next day and begin working on his invention.

9. IN HIS laboratory, Breville set to work on a series of sandwich toasting experiments. However, progress was difficult. The smooth toasting plates on his prototypes stubbornly remained too easy to clean. The disillusioned inventor decided to go for a walk to clear his mind.

10. IN A BELGRADE park, Breville trod in some dog dirt. He wiped the sole of his shoe on some grass, poked it with a twig and even trod in puddles but still failed to get rid of all the excrement from the tread. "Eureka!" cried the inventor. "This turd has given me the solution to my problem!"

11. BACK IN his laboratory, Breville made a pair of new toasting plates with a heavily convoluted surface like the sole of his shoe. Nervously, he toasted a sandwich and examined the results. Like the faeces in the park, the burnt cheese had stuck fast to the plates and proved almost impossible to remove. Success at last!

12. BUT MORE development work was needed before the toaster was ready to go on the market. Early versions proved too large to stick in the back of a cupboard and forget about. Breville worked hard producing a version compact enough to fit snugly behind flasks, stray saucepan lids and buckled tupperware boxes.

13. BREVILLE tested his new invention on volunteers who eagerly made one or two sandwiches, before deciding the device was more trouble than it was worth. It was launched at the 1904 Heidelberg Kitchen Gadgetry, Miracle Mops and Dripless Painting System Exposition.

14. THE BREVILLE sandwich toaster was an immediate success. The 8 billion Brevilles sold worldwide since its invention have between them toasted up to 16 billion sandwiches, and it is widely regarded as the world's best-selling and most used a couple of times and then put in the back of the cupboard invention.

Next Week - *The Fuzzaway -How Sir Alfred Remington's invention made pill balls a thing of the past until the batteries ran down and it got put in a drawer.*

WILL MICHAEL JACKSON SURVIVE HIS FATAL HEART ATTACK?
DON'T MISS PART 2 OF THE MICHAEL JACKSON STORY

THIS YEAR, THE COUNTRY WAS GRIPPED BY THE TRAGIC STORY OF THE WHALE IN THE THAMES. BUT THIS WAS NOT THE FIRST TIME THAT ONE OF THESE CREATURES HAS SWUM UP THE CAPITAL'S RIVER AND INTO THE NATION'S HEART. LET ME TAKE YOU BACK OVER SIXTY YEARS AND TELL YOU THE TRUE STORY OF...

REAL LIFE 'DR DOOLITTLE' JOHNNY MORRIS'S ANIMAL TALES

THE WHALE OF WORLD WAR II

1945 AND THE WAR IS GOING WELL FOR BRITAIN. ALTHOUGH LONDON HAS BEEN BOMBED BY HITLER'S LUFTWAFFE, SPIRITS ARE HIGH THANKS TO THE ANTICS OF WELLINGTON, A 100 FOOT SPERM WHALE WHO HAS MADE HIS HOME UNDER TOWER BRIDGE.

THREE CHEERS FOR LONDON'S WHALE!

THIS PERISHING LEVIATHAN HAS UNIFIED US LONDONERS GOOD AND PROPER AND NO MISTAKE.

YOU AIN'T WRONG AN' ALL YOU AIN'T. NOT WHILE WE'VE GOT WELLINGTON TO WARM OUR COCKLES.

BUT ONE MAN IN LONDON WAS NOT CELEBRATING THE PRESENCE OF THE 300 TON VISITOR...

HMM! I SINK MEIN FUHRER SHOULD KNOW ABOUT ZIS WHALE.

IN A SECRET BUNKER IN GERMANY.

ICH BIN DAS LONDON AGENT ON DAS BLOWER, MEIN FUHRER.

MINE GOODNESS MICHT. VOT DOES HE VONT, EIN VONDER.

FUHRER! ZERE IST A VHALE IN ZE THAMES, UND IT IS BOOSTING ZE MORALE OF ZE LONDONERS LIKE NOTHINK I HEF EVER SEEN...

GOTT IN HIMMEL!

OLD UND YOUNG, RRRICH UND POOR, CATHOLIC UND PRRRODESTANT...ALL ARE UNITED IN ZERE LOVE FOR VELLINGTON ZE VHALE

ZE FARTERLAND VILL NEVER DEFEAT ZE ALLIES WHILE VELLINGTON LIVES!

MEIN GOTT!

NEVER HEF I SEEN SUCH UNITY IN A PEOPLE...

THE FUHRER IMMEDIATELY GATHERED THE FINEST BRAINS HIS WAR MACHINE HAD TO OFFER AND SET ABOUT DECIDING HOW TO KILL THE MORALE BOOSTING-CREATURE.

SO ZAT, GENTLEMEN, IST ZE PROBLEM. VE MUST SOLVE IT OR FOR US, ZE VOR IST OVER.

FIRST TO SPEAK WAS ROCKET PIONEER WERNER VON BRAUN.

MEIN FUHRER! VE SHOULD BLAST VIS WRRRETCHED BEAST OUT OF ZE VORTER VIS MEIN DOODLEBUGS!

A GOOD IDEA, HERR VON BRAUN.

FORGIVE ME, MEIN FUHRER, BUT ZE SPERM VHALE HAS SKIN DREI FEET THICK UND AS HARD AS CONCRRRETE. EIN DOODLEBUG WOULD MERELY BOUNCE OFF HIS BACK.

DR MENGELE, DO YOU HAVE ANY SUGGESTIONS?

I SINK VE SHOULD SEND A CRACK TEAM OF DIVERS TO SVIM UP ZE THAMES UND HAMMER A CORK INTO HIS BLOW HOLE.

HMMM...

NO, HERR MENGELE. DER SPUNKENVHALE HAS A BLOWHOLE ELEVEN UND A HALF INCHES ACROSS. VERE VOULD VE GET A CORK ZAT BIG?

OH!?! ZEN VOT IF OUR LONDON AGENT SCHNUCK DOWN TO ZEE RIVER AT NIGHT UND FED THE VHALE VIS ZE POISONED PLANKTON?

FIRSTLICHT, EIN SPUNKENVHALE DOES NOT FEED IN ZE DARKNESS UND SECONDLICHT, IT DOES NOT EAT PLANKTON. ITS PRINCIPAL DIET CONSISTS OF SQVID.

YOU SEEM TO KNOW A LOT ABOUT ZE VHALES, MEIN HERR. WHO ARE YOU?

ICH BIN DR GUNTHER KNOCKWURST OF THE BERLIN OCEANOGRAPHICAL INSTITUTE, MEIN FUHRER, UND I KNOW ZERE IS ONLY VON VAY TO KILL ZAT VHALE UND VIN ZE VOR!

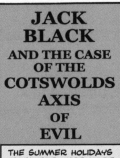

JACK BLACK
AND THE CASE OF THE COTSWOLDS AXIS OF EVIL

THE SUMMER HOLIDAYS WERE HERE ONCE MORE. JUNIOR SLEUTH JACK BLACK AND SILVER, HIS DETECTIVE DOG, HAD COME TO STAY WITH AUNT MEG AT HER CANAL-SIDE NEWSAGENTS IN THE PRETTY GLOUCESTERSHIRE VILLAGE OF BARTRAM-ON-THE-WATER.

COME INSIDE, JACK. I'VE GOT SOMETHING TO SHOW YOU.

WHAT IS IT?

AREN'T THEY ADORABLE, JACK?

PLEASE CAN I KEEP ONE?

NO. I'VE GOT TO DROWN EVERY LAST ONE OF THEM, I'M AFRAID

CAN'T YOU WAIT UNTIL I GET BACK FROM MY PAPER ROUND?

SORRY, JACK. I'VE GOT TO GET THEM SKINNED AND MADE INTO GONKS FOR MY TOY STALL AT THE VILLAGE FETE THIS AFTERNOON.

GOSH YES! THE VILLAGE FETE! SAMSON AND DELILAH, THE BIGGEST TRACTION ENGINES IN THE COTSWOLDS ARE GOING TO BE THERE. I CAN'T WAIT TO SEE THEM.

WELL, YOU WON'T GET TO SEE THEM UNTIL YOU'VE DELIVERED ALL THESE PAPERS, MY LAD.

OH, AND DON'T FORGET TO CALL BY THAT NEW SHOP ON THE HIGH STREET AND SEE IF THE MAN WANTS TO PLACE AN ORDER.

RIGHTY-HO, AUNT MEG!

JACK AND SILVER MADE SHORT WORK OF THEIR ROUND, AND SOON ARRIVED AT THE NEW SHOP...

RUSHBRIDGER'S VEGETARIAN WHOLEFOOD

NOW OPEN!

OH, HELLO THERE. I THOUGHT YOU WERE THE POSTMAN. I'M EXPECTING A PARCEL THIS MORNING.

I'M JACK BLACK AND THIS IS MY DOG, SILVER. MY AUNT MEG RUNS THE NEWSAGENTS IN THE VILLAGE.

WELL, WELCOME TO MY WHOLE FOOD SHOP, JACK. WOULD YOU LIKE TO TRY A SLICE OF SEED CAKE? IT'S DELICIOUS!

EEURGH! NO THANKS! THAT'S BUDGIE FOOD.

GRRRR!

AUNT MEG WANTS TO KNOW IF YOU'D LIKE TO PLACE AN ORDER FOR A DAILY PAPER.

OH, YES PLEASE, JACK.

SMASHING. ONE DAILY MAIL IT IS, THEN.

OH NO, NOT THE MAIL. I'LL HAVE THE GUARDIAN PLEASE. OR THE INDEPENDENT PERHAPS

JACK HAD HEARD ENOUGH.

SORRY! I'VE GOT TO GO NOW...

DID YOU HEAR THAT, BOY? HE DIDN'T WANT THE DAILY MAIL. EVERYBODY IN THE VILLAGE GETS THE MAIL.

COME ON, LET'S GO AND SEE PC BROWN!

SHORTLY...

...DIDN'T WANT THE MAIL, YOU SAY? WELL, THERE'S NOT REALLY A GREAT DEAL I CAN DO ABOUT THAT, JACK. IT'S A FREE COUNTRY, I'M AFRAID.

HE WANTED THE GUARDIAN!

WELL, I'VE HEARD OF PEOPLE LIKE THIS, BUT UNFORTUNATELY THERE'S NO LAW AGAINST IT.

BUT HE DOESN'T EAT MEAT, PC BROWN!

NEITHER DID HITLER, JACK.

HMMM, I SUPPOSE...

MR. RUSHBRIDGER'S PROBABLY JUST A HARMLESS ECCENTRIC. DON'T WORRY ABOUT HIM.

BUT JACK WAS WORRIED. SOMETHING ABOUT THE NEW-COMER HAD MADE HIM SUSPICIOUS.

PC BROWN MIGHT NOT BE INTERESTED IN THE GOINGS-ON AT RUSHBRIDGER'S SHOP, SILVER, BUT I AM.

SEEN SOMETHING SUSPICIOUS OR A COLOURED? CALL 999!

REMEMBER HE SAID HE WAS WAITING FOR A PARCEL? COME ON, BOY; LET'S CATCH THE POSTMAN BEFORE HE MAKES HIS DELIVERY!

JACK AND SILVER CAUGHT THE POSTIE JUST IN TIME, AND TOLD HIM ALL ABOUT THE MYSTERIOUS VEGETARIAN SHOP-KEEPER WHO DIDN'T WANT THE DAILY MAIL...

YOU'RE RIGHT. IT DOES SOUND A BIT OF A RUM DO, YOUNG JACK

HERE'S HIS PARCEL. LET'S OPEN IT.

BUT WHAT THEY FOUND RAISED MORE QUESTIONS THAN IT ANSWERED!

FOUR ENGINE DRIVERS' HATS?

WHAT WOULD A FOOD SHOP OWNER WANT WITH THESE?

IT JUST DOESN'T MAKE ANY SENSE.

COME ON, SILVER. THERE'S DETECTIVE WORK TO BE DONE

THE CRIME-BUSTING DUO WASTED NO TIME AND WERE SOON SNEAKING INTO THE VEGETARIAN'S PREMISES.

WE'RE IN LUCK, BOY. RUSHBRIDGER'S LEFT A WINDOW OPEN. NOW'S OUR CHANCE TO HAVE A GOOD LOOK AROUND.

RUSHBRIDGERS DELIVERIES

WHAT IS IT, BOY? WHAT HAVE YOU FOUND?

WOW! IT'S A SECRET TRAPDOOR. I WONDER WHAT HE'S HIDING DOWN THERE?

GOSH! IT'S AN AL QUAEDA CELL...AND THEY'RE PLOTTING A TERRORIST OUTRAGE AT THIS AFTERNOON'S VILLAGE FETE!

WHISPER, WHISPER...

WE'VE GOT TO TELL PC BROWN! LET'S GO!

I'M AFRAID YOU'RE GOING NOWHERE...

...EXCEPT INTO THIS CELLAR!

GOSH! MR. RUSHBRIDGER!

IN A TRICE, THE EVIL SHOPKEEPER HAD JACK TRUSSED UP LIKE A CHICKEN...

RIGHT, WE'RE OFF TO COMMIT OUR ATROCITY AT THE VILLAGE FETE...

...AND THERE'S ABSOLUTELY NOTHING YOU AND YOUR FLEA-RIDDEN MUTT CAN DO TO STOP US! HA-HA-HA!

HO! HO! HO!

THE GOLDEN ARCHES OF COURAGE

THE ANNALS OF FAST FOOD ARE FULL OF TALES OF BRAVERY AND DERRING-DO. AND NONE MORE SO THAN THIS STORY OF YOUNG JOHNNY JOHNSON - A TABLE WIPER WHO FOUND THE STRENGTH WITHIN HIMSELF TO OVERCOME THE ODDS...

CHRISTMAS EVE, 1998. FROM THE OUTSIDE, ALL SEEMED QUIET AT THE WESTERN FRONT RETAIL PARK MACDONALDS...BUT INSIDE, THE STAFF WERE BEGINNING TO GET TENSE...

IT'S QUIET... TOO QUIET.

I WISH I WAS BACK HOME.

DON'T WORRY, CHALKIE. ALL THIS PERISHIN' PALAVER'LL BE OVER BY CHRISTMAS DAY.

WELL, IT MAY SEEM QUIET NOW, BUT WHEN THOSE SHOPS CLOSE AT HALF PAST FIVE WE'RE GOING TO GET WAVE AFTER WAVE OF CHRISTMAS SHOPPERS COMING THROUGH THOSE DOORS.

IT'S GOING TO BE HELL, DO YOU HEAR ME? HELL!...

...BUT IF WE ALL REMEMBER WHAT WE WERE TAUGHT IN BASIC TRAINING, WE'LL ALL GET THROUGH THIS THING IN ONE PIECE.

RIGHT, CHAPS. 5.25, TIME FOR ONE LAST CHECK OF THE EQUIPMENT.

OIL UP TO TEMPERATURE...CHECK! NAPKIN MAGAZINES FULLY CHARGED...CHECK! MCNUGGET HOPPERS LOADED...CHECK!

OH, HELLO THERE. ER....JOHNSON, ISN'T IT? EVERYTHING ALRIGHT, SON?

I'M....I'M SCARED, MR RENTON. THIS IS MY FIRST CHRISTMAS AT MCDONALDS.

WELL, SON, THIS IS MY SIXTH CHRISTMAS HERE, AND GUESS WHAT...

...I'M TERRIFIED.

REALLY!? BUT YOU'VE GOT FIVE STARS, MR RENTON.

WELL, I'LL LET YOU IN ON A LITTLE SECRET, JOHNSON. WHEN THE CUSTOMERS START COMING THROUGH THAT DOOR FIRING THEIR ORDERS AT US, THESE STARS WON'T COUNT FOR DIDDLY SQUAT.

YOU JUST DO YOUR JOB, JOHNSON, AND STAY FOCUSED. KEEP GIVING THOSE TABLES A CURSORY WIPE WITH YOUR GREASY CLOTH, SON, AND YOU'LL DO JUST FINE.

YES, MR RENTON

OKAY! LOOKS LIKE THE TIME FOR TALKING IS OVER...

GOOD LUCK, SON!

INCOMING!!

STATIONS EVERYBODY! GO! GO! GO!

WELCOME TO MCDONALDS. CAN I TAKE YOUR ORDER, PLEASE?

EAT IN OR TAKE OUT?

EAT IN.

THREE HAPPY MEALS. TWO BOY'S NUGGETS, ONE GIRL'S BURGER. COKE WITH ALL THREE. BIG MAC AND A THICK SHAKE. STRAWBERRY.

TWO BIG MAC MEALS. LARGE. NINE MCNUGGETS AND LARGE FRIES. THREE COKES.

WELCOME TO MCDONALDS. CAN I TAKE YOUR ORDER, PLEASE?

GINGER! BOX OF NINE TO TILL THREE! AND FAST!

BETTER GET YOURSELF TO MR RENTON'S OFFICE, LET SOMEONE HAVE A LOOK AT THAT EYE.

NO! NO TIME FOR THAT. I'VE GOT TO FETCH THAT KETCHUP!

EVENTUALLY. JOHNNY REACHED THE BACK OF THE KITCHEN.

THERE IT IS! IF I CAN... JUST REACH...

BUT...

AAIEEE!!

GROAN! MY LEGS! I...CAN'T FEEL ...MY...LEGS!

TWO MINUTES LATER...

CHEESEBURGER WITH LARGE FRIES AND A DONUT. AND A FANTA.

ARE YOU GETTING THAT BLOODY TOMATO SAUCE OR WHAT?

TSK!

LOOKS LIKE THE LITTLE CHAP DIDN'T MAKE IT.

MR RENTON! LOOK!

WHA...!?!

HNNNG! HNNNG!

GOOD GOD! JOHNSON!

I MADE IT! COUGH! COUGH! I MADE IT ...DIDN'T I, MR RENTON?

YOU CERTAINLY DID, JOHNSON! YOU CERTAINLY DID!

12.30AM.

GOOD NIGHT, EVERYONE.

GOOD NIGHT. MERRY CHRISTMAS!

AND YOU. MERRY CHRISTMAS!

WELL, THAT'S YOUR FIRST CHRISTMAS EVE AT MCDONALDS OVER, JOHNSON.

YES, MR RENTON COUGH! COUGH!

AND I'VE GOT A LITTLE SOMETHING FOR YOU!

WHAT YOU DID TONIGHT WAS SOMETHING SPECIAL, JOHNSON!

I'M MAKING YOU EMPLOYEE OF THE MONTH!

EMPLOYEE OF THE MONTH

DECEMBER

JOHNNY JOHNSON

GOSH!

BUT JOHNNY WAS IN FOR A BIGGER SURPRISE!

AND I THINK YOU'VE EARNED THIS, TOO.

A STAR! MY FIRST STAR!

ONE DAY I'LL HAVE FIVE, MR RENTON. JUST LIKE YOU.

I'M SURE YOU WILL, JOHNSON. HA! HA! I'M SURE YOU WILL!

BUT YOUNG JOHNNY JOHNSON NEVER GOT THE CHANCE TO EARN THOSE STARS. FOR JUST TWO DAYS LATER, ON BOXING DAY 1998, HE TURNED UP FOR WORK FOUR MINUTES LATE; AND MR RENTON WAS FORCED TO SACK HIM ON THE SPOT. BUT HIS TALE OF BRAVERY BEYOND THE CALL OF DUTY IS STILL TOLD TODAY IN MCDONALDS STAFF ROOMS ACROSS THE WORLD.

The Story

Although nowadays we imagine it is a modern phenomenon for children to spend twenty-three hours each day playing Tomb Raider 4, such behaviour has been traced back to ancient Egypt. Boy king Tutankhamen ordered the special construction of a dark, airless bedroom in which - in the afterlife - he intended to spend all eternity playing computer games. However, the young Pharaoh's plans came to nothing as, shortly after his death, real-life tomb raiders broke into the room - the Great Pyramid of Cheops - and stole his mummified PlayStation, which they later sold at a car boot sale for £5.

Though we may not realise it, over the last twenty years computers have taken control of our world. Whether they're unexpectedly plunging air traffic control into lethal chaos, whether they're sending us wildly inaccurate bills and bank statements, or whether they're simply allowing us to instantaneously e-mail the man at the next desk sick jokes about recently-deceased celebrities, they have become an indispensible part of all our lives.

But the story of computers goes back much further than you may think. Indeed, to understand the origins of today's most modern technology we must step back in time almost one million years to stone age Wiltshire.

Until recent times, mystery shrouded the reasons why primitive men hauled the enormous lumps of stone that form Stonehenge onto the plains of what is now Salisbury. It was not until the the last century that archaeologists discovered that the strange monolithic structure is actually the world's first known computer. The stone circle is carefully aligned with the heavens, so that at midnight on the Winter and Spring solstices, the planets Venus and Saturn appear ringed by stars, forming a massive pair of breasts.

Many archaeologists believe that the 70 ton central 'Heel Stone' could have been a primitive mouse. Calculations however, suggest it would have taken 600 men to move it around, and another 40 to double click it.

Many millenniums later, computers reappeared on the other side of the world, but built for a very different purpose.

The next serious attempt to build a computer didn't take place until 1822, when mathematician Charles Babbage began work on his Difference Engine. His revolutionary device carried out different computational functions according to information stored on punched cards. In 1824 it broke down and he took it into the Basingstoke branch of Difference Engine World to be repaired. However, staff at the shop called police when they discovered over 1500 pornographic images of chimney sweep's boys and little matchgirls stored in the machine's cogs.

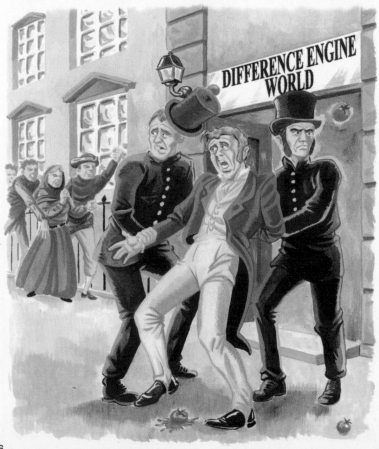

f the Computer

Necessity is the mother of invention, and during World War 2, the nazis' invention of the supposedly uncrackable Enigma code machine spurred on the development of digital computers. At the top secret Bletchley Park establishment, mathematician Alan Turing developed a prototype programmable computer - the Colossus - with which he was able to decipher intercepted German messages.

Meanwhile on another continent, 8-year-old Korean schoolboy Yon Sung Non was up in his bedroom perfecting his Colossus-Fucker 2 computer virus. The unsuspecting Turing loaded the bug onto the Bletchley main-frame whilst trying to install Donkey Kong from a disc he had been lent by a man in a pub. The allied war effort was set back 2 years, leading to the deaths of an estimated 3,000,000 people, whilst Turing switched his jammed computer on and off at the wall.

Twenty years later necessity was still the mother of invention when President Kennedy vowed to put a man on the Moon by the end of the sixties. By today's standards, the state-of-the-art machinery used then looks woefully inadequate. Indeed, it has been estimated that the tiny personal organiser in your pocket is thirty times as powerful as the entire network of computers used by NASA to put Neil Armstrong on the lunar surface.

In 1969, the Apollo 13 astronauts narrowly avoided disaster when the overtaxed computers at Mission Control jammed for three days whilst NASA engineers, armed only with Buzz Aldrin's credit card,

desperately battled to download a home video of Jayne Mansfield sucking off Bing Crosby. On a boat.

Impressive though the Appollo moonshots were, perhaps the most remarkable achievement of information technology in recent years is that it has transformed a humourless, bespectacled, pasty-faced streak of piss into the richest, most influential and most powerful man on the planet.

Bill Gates, who spent the first 25 years of his life wanking in his bedroom amongst a pile of takeaway pizza boxes, now has a personal fortune estimated at a cool 750 million billion billion dollars - that's fifteen times as much money as there is in the world.

But it's the average man's daily life which has been changed most by the technological revolution. Thanks to computers taking over thousands of highly complex skilled jobs in offices and factories, people have been liberated from the drudgery of going out to work and are now free to spend their days lying in bed watching daytime television, whilst their old jobs are done more efficiently, cheaply and quickly by beige plastic boxes.

But what of the future? The one thing experts are agreed on is that it's in the field of memory that the developments are going to be most dramatic. Indeed, scientists predict that by the year 2020 computers with 10 million billion gigabytes of RAM will be commonplace. This means an ordinary lap-top no bigger than a Weetabix will be able to store enough hardcore pornography for everybody in China to have two thousand wanks.

Don't miss next week, Facktfinders, when Dr. Fackt chronicles the story of smegma.

JACK BLACK
AND THE CASE OF THE LORD MAYOR'S CHAIN

THE SUMMER HOLIDAYS WERE HERE ONCE MORE AND JACK BLACK, THE BOY DETECTIVE, AND HIS FAITHFUL CANINE SIDEKICK SILVER, WERE STAYING WITH AUNT MEG IN THE PICTURESQUE CORNISH LOBSTER FISHING VILLAGE OF ST TRELAWNY.

SILVER AND I ARE OFF TO THE QUAY SIDE TO DO A BIT OF CRABBING, AUNT MEG.

THAT'S NICE, JACK...

...BY THE WAY, HAVE YOU HEARD THE BIG NEWS IN THE VILLAGE?

THE LORD MAYOR'S CHAIN HAS BEEN STOLEN AGAIN.

WHAT!?! THAT'S THE THIRD TIME IN AS MANY WEEKS. HE NO SOONER REPLACES IT THAN IT GETS STOLEN.

I KNOW.

THIS LOOKS LIKE A JOB FOR ME AND YOU, SILVER. COME ON, BOY, THERE'S DETECTIVE WORK TO DO.

NO, THERE'S NO NEED TO BOTHER YOURSELVES...

WOOF!

...THE FABULOUS FOUR HAVE GOT THE CASE ALL TIED UP

THE FABULOUS FOUR!?! WHO THE RUDDY HECK ARE THEY WHEN THEY'RE AT HOME?

THEY'RE THREE INTREPID JUNIOR CRIME FIGHTERS - FREDDIE, GEORGE AND BUNTY, AND THEIR LITTLE YORKSHIRE TERRIER, PARKIE.

THEY'RE STAYING NEXT DOOR WITH THEIR AUNT PAT FOR THE SUMMER HOLIDAYS. THEY'VE BEEN DOING A LOT OF DETECTIVE WORK AND BY ALL ACCOUNTS THEY HAVE THE CASE OF THE LORD MAYOR'S CHAIN AS GOOD AS SOLVED.

HAVE THEY INDEED?

YES. APPARENTLY A GANG OF SMUGGLERS STOLE THE CHAINS AND MELTED THEM DOWN INTO LITTLE INGOTS IN THE OLD ABANDONED LIGHTHOUSE...

...DISGUISING THEMSELVES AS GHOSTS TO SCARE OFF ANYONE WHO GOT SUSPICIOUS ABOUT THE ACTIVITY ON THE ISLAND...

...THEN FED THE GOLD INGOTS TO SPECIALLY-BRED METAL-EATING LOBSTERS WHICH THEY THEN RELEASED INTO THE SEA...

...MR STROMBOLI, THE RINGMASTER FROM THE CIRCUS, THEN DISGUISED HIMSELF AS A FISHER-MAN AND SAILED OUT UNDER COVER OF DARKNESS TO LAY LOBSTER TRAPS IN THE HARBOUR...

CALYPSO

...USING A SPECIALLY-TRAINED TROUPE OF CIRCUS MONKEYS TO RAISE THE TRAPS THE FOLLOWING EVENING.

THE LOBSTERS WERE THEN SMASHED OPEN AND THE PRECIOUS GOLDEN NUGGETS WITHIN WERE SOLD TO A GANG OF INTERNATIONAL CRIMINALS MASQUERADING AS A VISITING BAVARIAN OOMPAH BAND...

...WHO HID THE GOLD IN THEIR EUPHONIUMS, AND THEN FEIGNED TOOTHACHE SO AS THEY COULD VISIT THE DENTIST WITHOUT AROUSING SUSPICION...

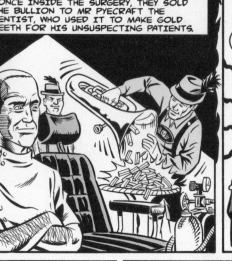

...ONCE INSIDE THE SURGERY, THEY SOLD THE BULLION TO MR PYECRAFT THE DENTIST, WHO USED IT TO MAKE GOLD TEETH FOR HIS UNSUSPECTING PATIENTS.

YES, IT WAS SOME PRETTY GOOD DETECTIVE WORK THEY DID.

BUT, I'M THE BOY DETECTIVE IN THIS VILLAGE, AUNT MEG. IT SHOULD BE ME SOLVING THAT MYSTERY...

...NOT SOME BUNCH OF TUPPENNY HA'PENNY JOHNNY-COME-LATELIES!

WELL, THEY'VE BEATEN YOU TO IT, JACK. THEY'VE JUST ONE MORE PIECE OF EVIDENCE TO GATHER, THEN I UNDERSTAND THEY'RE GOING TO EXPOSE THE PLOT TOMORROW...

...WHEN PC BROWN WILL ARREST MR PYECRAFT AND PUT HIM IN PRISON.

HMM! I THINK WE SHOULD FOLLOW THEM, SILVER, AND SEE EXACTLY WHAT THEIR LITTLE PLAN IS.

GRRR!

THAT NIGHT, THE FABULOUS FOUR SET OUT ON THE LAST LEG OF THEIR CRIME-FIGHTING MISSION - LITTLE REALISING THEY HAD COMPANY!

COME ON, FREDDIE...

...LET'S GO AND GET OUR FINAL CLUE TO SOLVE THIS MYSTERY.

I'M COMING TOO.

YAP! YAP!

BUT YOU'RE JUST A GIRL.

SO? GIRLS CAN BE JUST AS GOOD AT DETECTING AS BOYS.

NO, THEY CAN'T.

STOP BICKERING, YOU TWO.

WE'LL NEVER GET TO SMUGGLERS' COVE AT THIS RATE.

SMUGGLERS' COVE, EH? SO THAT'S WHERE THEY'RE OFF TO!

COME ON, BOY.

SHORTLY.

THERE THEY GO. I WONDER WHAT THEY'RE LOOKING FOR.

INSIDE A CAVE AT THE FOOT OF THE CLIFF

LOOK HERE, EVERYONE, JUST AS I THOUGHT. LOBSTER TRAPS, SOME SMASHED LOBSTERS, A RINGMASTER'S OUTFIT, A BUNCH OF BANANAS, A TUBA AND AN APPOINTMENT CARD TO SEE MR PYECRAFT THE DENTIST.

GOSH! WE'VE GOT THOSE BADDIES BANG TO RIGHTS.

COME ON, SILVER. WE HAVE TO WARN THE ROBBERS BEFORE THE FABULOUS FOUR STEAL OUR THUNDER.

THE GHOST OF JAMES HUNT'S TRUE MOTOR SPORT TALES

The JOHNNY CHICANE Story

THE 1950'S, HEYDAY OF GRAND PRIX MOTOR RACING, WHEN DEVIL-MAY-CARE HEROES SUCH AS FANGIO AND MOSS REGULARLY ROLLED THE DICE OF DEATH, RACING WHEEL TO WHEEL RIGHT UP TO THE CHEQUERED FLAG. THE PRICE WAS OFTEN HIGH AND MANY A DRIVER NEVER LIVED TO TELL THE TALE OF HIS HIGH SPEED ADVENTURES. ONE SUCH WAS JOHNNY CHICANE, AND THIS IS HIS STORY...

BRANDS HATCH, 1955, AND THE GRAND PRIX SEASON WAS REACHING ITS CLIMAX.

WELL DONE, JOHNNY. ANOTHER POLE POSITION. WIN TOMORROWS FINAL RACE OF THE SEASON AND YOU'LL BE WORLD CHAMPION. YOU JUST NEED TO FINISH AHEAD OF YOUR ARCH RIVAL, MANFRED VON COBBLERS.

THANKS, MR BARNTON, BUT IF I DO, IT'LL BE DOWN TO THE CAR. SHE'S RUNNING LIKE A DREAM.

YOU SHOULD BE PROUD OF YOURSELF, TOMMY. I RECKON THE BARNTON SPECIAL'S JUST ABOUT UNBEATABLE, THANKS TO YOUR HARD WORK IN THE PITS.

THANKS, JOHNNY.

ANYWAY, I'M OFF FOR A CUP OF TEA AND A BIT OF SHUT-EYE BEFORE TOMORROWS RACE.

ME TOO.

OH TOMMY, CHANGE THE OIL AND SPARKPLUGS, TUNE UP THE CARBURETTOR AND GREASE THE AXLES, WILL YOU? THERE'S A GOOD FELLOW.

YEAH, OFF YOU GO, CHICANE. HAVE A GOOD NIGHT'S SLEEP.

IT'LL BE THE LAST ONE YOU'LL EVER HAVE. HE-HE-HE!

SUDDENLY A FIGURE EMERGED FROM THE SHADOWS.

NICHT ZO LOUD, DUMBKOPF! HE MIGHT HEAR YOU!

MR VON COBBLERS! I DIDN'T SEE YOU THERE.

JA. ZAT'S BECAUSE I VOS HIDINK IN ZE SHADOWS. ANY VAY, ICH BIN HERE TO MAKE SURE YOU KNOW EXACTLY VOT TO DO DURINK ZE RACE.

DON'T WORRY, MR VON COBBLERS, I KNOW EXACTLY VOT I'VE GOT TO DO. I'M GOING TO CUT THE BRAKE CABLES ON CHICANE'S CAR.

JA! PUTTINK HIM OUT OF ZE RACE UND GIVINK ME ZE VURLD TITLE! HA!

SHALL I SNIP THEM AT THE START OF THE RACE?

NEIN, TOMMY. DO IT DURINK HIS FINAL PIT STOP. ICH DON'T VONT MEIN CHAMPIONSHIP-VINNINK VICTORY TO LOOK TOO EASY.

OKAY, CONSIDER IT DONE. NOW WHERE'S MY MONEY?

HERE, EIN TEN SHILLINK NOTE.

TEN BOB?! HERE, A POUND YOU SAID.

PATIENCE, MEIN OLD CHUM. YOU'LL GET ZE REST VENN I TAKE ZE CHEQUERED FLAG IN MEIN TURBOCHARGED MENGELEMOBILE TOMORROW AFTERNOON.

THE NEXT DAY, THE DRIVERS LINED UP ON THE GRID FOR THE START OF THE BRITISH GRAND PRIX.

SEE YOU AT THE FINISHING LINE, COBBLERS OLD THING. I'LL HAVE A GLASS OF BUBBLY READY FOR YOU.

ZAT'S VOT YOU SINK, CHICANE.

GENTLEMEN, START YOUR ENGINES... READY... STEADY...

GO!!

AND THEY'RE OFF! CHICANE IN THE BARNTON SPECIAL TAKES AN EARLY LEAD...

VROOOOMMM!!

FROM THE START, JOHNNY SHOWED HIS CLASS, PUTTING PLENTY OF TRACK BETWEEN HIM AND HIS TEUTONIC RIVAL.

CHICANE IS SETTING A BLISTERING PACE!

BRRR-OWN!

AND AT HIS FIRST PIT STOP AFTER 20 LAPS, THE PLUCKY BRIT ALREADY HAD A COMMANDING LEAD.

HOW AM I DOING, MR BARNTON?

GREAT, JOHNNY, GREAT. YOU'VE PUT THIRTY SECONDS BETWEEN YOU AND VON COBBLERS.

YOU'VE NOT GOT ENOUGH FUEL ON BOARD TO GET TO THE END OF THE RACE. PIT AGAIN WITH ONE LAP TO GO.

RIGHT YOU ARE!

THE CROWD THRILLED AS CHICANE'S CAR EASILY KEPT ITS LEAD DURING THE SECOND STINT.

WOW! THIS CAR'S FLYING TODAY!

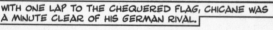

WITH ONE LAP TO THE CHEQUERED FLAG, CHICANE WAS A MINUTE CLEAR OF HIS GERMAN RIVAL.

NICE DRIVING, JOHNNY. JUST A SPLASH AND DASH, AND THE WORLD CHAMPIONSHIP WILL BE YOURS.

ERM...HANG ON, I DON'T THINK THE BOOT'S SHUT PROPERLY.

UNSEEN, THE EVIL MECHANIC DID HIS WORK.

SNIGGER. THE EASIEST POUND I EVER EARNED.

OFF YOU GO, JOHNNY. LET'S SEE YOU SET A NEW LAP RECORD UP TO THE FINISH LINE!

LEAVE IT TO ME, MR BARNTON.

CRIKEY! I'M DOING 150! I'LL BRAKE LATE INTO THE HAIRPIN AND CUT THE KERB TO TAKE THE RACING LINE.

BUT...

WHAT THE...?! THE BRAKES! THEY'RE NOT WORKING!

I CAN'T CONTROL IT!

SCREEECHH!!

OH NO! CHICANES CRASHED ON HIS FINAL LAP!

WAH!

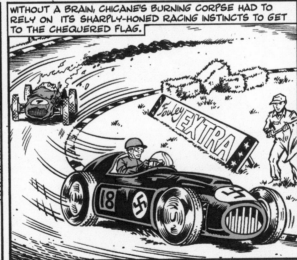

AS FOR THE REST, MANFRED VON COBBLERS GAVE UP DRIVING TO BECOME A RETAIL TOBACCONIST IN DORTMUND. HE DIED AFTER AN INGROWING TOENAIL WENT SEPTIC IN 1973.

MECHANIC TOMMY GREEN NEVER RECEIVED HIS SECOND TEN SHILLING NOTE, TURNED TO THE BOTTLE AND BECAME A HOPELESS ALCOHOLIC. HE NOW WORKS AS AN AIRLINE PILOT, FLYING LONG HAUL ACROSS THE ATLANTIC.

BARNTON RACING CONTINUED UNTIL THE EARLY 1960'S, WHEN EDDIE BARNTON PACKED IT ALL IN TO HAVE A SEX CHANGE. IN THE FOLLOWING DECADES, AS DUSTY SPRINGFIELD, HE HAD MANY TOP TEN HITS INCLUDING 'YOU DON'T HAVE TO SAY YOU LOVE ME', 'SON OF A PREACHER MAN' AND 'WHAT HAVE I DONE TO DESERVE THIS' (WITH THE PET SHOP BOYS)

READ AND DESPAIR

The Wonderful

THE ADVERTISING profession is surely the most creative of disciplines, skilfully combining art, poetry, theatre and music. The advertisers skilfully show us how we can solve problems that don't actually exist by getting us to spend money we don't have on things we don't need or want. Without them, we wouldn't know what to buy. How would we know if we wanted a Citroen AX or a Renault Clio without the help of Papa and Nicole? The whole economy would grind to a halt, and society would plunge into chaos.

Let's take a look at how a typical product is marketed...

Picture 1
The day starts early for Chad Nadbag, a successful Account Executive with top City Advertising agency NDP, DPD, Bugle, Beagle, Buggery. The creative brain does not run on thin air, so it's out of bed and into the bathroom for the day's first line of grade A cocaine. With his mind up to speed, it's time for the day's first creative dilemma. After two hours and twenty cups of coffee, the decision is made - Spotty braces, orange horn-rimmed glasses and Teletubbies bow tie.

Picture 4
Eventually, after weeks of brainstorming, the creative team return, mentally exhausted but jubilant. At a presentation, they reveal the name concept

Picture 6
The team decide to target their campaign at chocolate-eating ABC1's aged 18-35. After three months in The Maldives, they decide to nick that scene from '9½ Weeks' and have a young scantily-clad couple feed each other Choc-o-Bars in front of an open fridge. So it's off to New York for a month where the entire team have to be present on set to make sure everything goes to plan.

Picture 7
Six months later and the campaign is over. At a series of champagne and coke-fuelled backslapping ceremonies, the team responsible for the 'Choc-o-Bar' launch win a series of prestigious awards. Best above the line brand identity concept; Most creatively original full client package; Best account brief realisation for confectionery product beginning with 'C', are just three of the awards it takes at the worthless 'British Advertising and Marketing Industry Awards' wankfest at a fancy London hotel.

Picture 2

At any one time, a successful agency will be working on many different accounts, and the successful advertising executive must be able to apply himself to all creative styles. One minute he may be writing a bittersweet mini-drama for the Oxo family; the next, a riotous side-splitting double glazing advert for Reg Holdsworth. At this meeting, a marketing executive from a chocolate company wants the team to work on a campaign for a new chocolate bar.

Picture 3

The most most important thing in a successful campaign is branding - the right name can make or break a product. This 'brand identity conception process' is one of the biggest creative challenges in the marketing world. The right atmosphere must be established to ensure that the creative processes of the executives' minds are working at full throttle. So it's off to the West Indies for three months to think up the name.

of the new bar of chocolate to the client. It has taken many weeks and has already cost the client hundreds of thousands of pounds to get to this stage, and it is the turning point in the campaign. Happily the client is convinced, and 'Choc-o-Bar' is born. The campaign to sell it is underway.

Picture 5

It is the job of the advertising executive to make you think that your life is incomplete without a Choc-o-Bar. No matter how strong the brand identity concept is, it will not sell without an imaginative, eye-catching television push that must make an impact. A great idea for an advert is essential, and there is only one place great ideas come from. The executives must now spend weeks trawling their memories for famous scenes from films and comedy shows that they can steal in their entirety.

Picture 8

With a hatful of awards, the campaign has been a roaring success, making millions of pounds for the agency, and earning the team the respect of their peers. Outside the incestuous world of advertising, the campaign has made fuck-all impression on real people, as the client's pitiful sales graph shows. The team decide that not enough money was ploughed into the campaign, and that the only way to save the product is a complete brand rethink.

Picture 9

The whole creative process must start again, so it's off for another six months intensive 'Hothouse Brainstorming' in Trinidad and Tobago. But the pressure is on. If the new campaign for 'Bar-o-Choc' - like 'Choc-o-Bar' before it - fails, the team may be looking at nine months all-expenses-paid in Florida, with only half a ton of cocaine to assist the creative process.

Roy of CRESCENT NEWS

28 year old Roy Racey had only one dream, to become a paperboy for his local newsagents, Crescent News...

Perhaps today's the day I'll finally get to do a paper round

Timmy, you're on Armstrong Road. Number 6 is on holiday, so no papers there. And look out for the dog at number 14

Right, now go out there, lads and enjoy yourselves

What about me, boss?

Sorry, Roy, but you're reserve paperboy again

It's not fair, boss. All I need is a chance to show you I'm as good as any of them

Well, Jimmy Johnson's been on great form lately...

He got every paper in the right letter box yesterday. Including Mr Benson's Exchange and Mart

As Roy walked home he stopped at the statue of his Grandfather, a local hero...

My Grandad was the best paperboy this town ever had

And with his old bike, I'd be just as good as he was. If only Mr. Atkinson would pick me

JACKIE RACEY
1836 - 1905
PAPERBOY
AND
GENTLEM[AN]

Next morning, Roy arrived at Crescent News bright and early as usual...

Oh, dear! I'm sorry to hear that, Mrs. Johnson. I hope Jimmy's feeling better soon

What's wrong, Mr. Atkinson?

It's Jimmy Johnson. He's grazed his knee

How?

He fell off his bike going for a Daily Express in his bag. He'll be out for weeks

What am I going to do? It's Tuesday. Everyone's expecting their Radio Times and our star paperboy is out through injury. It's every manager's nightmare

I'll deliver them, Boss

You? I couldn't let you go out there today. I'd be throwing you in at the deep end

But, Boss. You've got no choice

Okay, Roy. Here's the papers. You're delivering for Crescent News

Thanks, Boss. I won't let you down

Bursting with pride, Roy slipped on the famous orange and black bag of Crescent News, as he had done a thousand times before in his dreams...

Crescent News is depending on you, Roy. Don't let us down

But in his eagerness as he left the shop...

Oh no! He's falling! I shouldn't have trusted an untried paperboy

I'll have to do the round myself in the car

Sorry, lad. The occasion has just proved too much for you. Come on, maybe next time, eh?

Please, Boss, give me another chance

I know I can deliver these papers.

Alright, lad. But we can't afford any more mistakes. If one of these papers were to fall into a puddle, well...

Don't worry. You can trust me

Pedalling like the wind, Roy set off on his round

His first newspaper was a textbook delivery...

the second went in with clinical accuracy...

followed seconds later by a third...

and a fourth!

But as the papers went in, Roy was unaware that he was being watched...

Hmmm! This new boy is good

Roy finished his round in record time

Yeah! Grandad would have been proud of me

Excuse me, sonny. Could I have a word?

Shortly...

Well done, Roy. Great delivery. How would you like to wear the black and orange bag tomorrow, and everyday?

Including Sundays

I'm asking you to deliver papers for Crescent News, lad. And I'm offering you £1.20 a week. What do you say?

Sorry, Mr. Atkinson. I can't

Allow me to introduce myself. I'm Ken Baxter, talent scout. I was impressed by your boy's strength, stamina and skill in all areas of delivery. I've snapped him up

But...

He's signed to City News in the precinct for £1.40 a week. He'll be wearing the famous red and white bag from now on

The following Saturday, Roy led the paperboys of City News out onto the precinct...

If only my Grandad was here to see me

The End

JACK BLACKSTERIX AND SILVMATIX

THE WILD BOAR MYSTERY

YOUNG JACK BLACKSTERIX WAS SPENDING THE EASTER HOLIDAYS WITH HIS AUNT MEGALITH, POST MISTRESS IN THE FIRST CENTURY GAULISH VILLAGE OF AQUASPUTUM...

MRS. TIMPSON WAS VERY GRATEFUL TO SEE HER PURSE AGAIN.

RIGHT. THERE'S NO TIME TO LOSE.

MOMENTS LATER, JACK HAD ALL THE EVIDENCE HE NEEDED.

COME ON, BOY. LETS GO!

SNAARL!!

NEXT MORNING...

HEY, JACK! WHERE ARE YOU OFF TO? YOU HAVEN'T HAD YOUR WEETABIXERIX YET.

NO TIME, AUNT MEGALITH. I'LL EXPLAIN LATER.

JACK AND HIS TRUSTY STEED WERE SOON HARING ACROSS THE GAULISH COUNTRYSIDE TOWARDS THE NEARBY ROMAN GARRISON...

HELLO THERE, MRS. CLERIHEW. WHAT'S HAPPENED TO YOU?

OH, A WOLF KILLED ALL MY CHICKENS LAST NIGHT, AND THEN ATTACKED ME.

ANYWAY, CAN'T STAND HERE TALKING. I'VE GOT THESE MEALS TO DELIVER.

NOT SO FAST, MRS. CLERIHEW!

THAT'S HER, CENTURION BROWN. SHE'S THE ONE WHO'S BEEN MAKING AND DISTRIBUTING MEALS TO THE OLD FOLK OF THE VILLAGE.

I SEE...

...AND WITHOUT A BASIC FOOD HYGIENE CERTIFICATE, I'LL BE BOUND.

BUT I HAVE GOT A CERTIFICATE. IT'S HANGING IN THE KITCHEN. I HAD TO GO ON A COURSE AND EVERYTHING.

AH!..ER...JACK?

YES, BUT YOU'VE CONTRAVENED THE TERMS OF THAT CERTIFICATE, HAVEN'T YOU, MRS. CLERIHEW?

HOW?

I SNEAKED INTO MRS. CLERIHEW'S HOUSE LAST NIGHT AND MOVED HER WASTE BIN SO THAT IT WAS WITHIN FIVE AND A HALF FEET OF THE TABLE. SECTION 3A OF THE FOOD HYGIENE REGULATIONS CLEARLY STATES THAT ALL WASTE RECEPTACLES MUST BE SITUATED AT LEAST SIX FEET FROM ANY FOOD PREPARATION.

YOU BITCH!! IT'S THE COLOSSEUM FOR YOU, CLERIHEW!!

AND IT'S THE COLOSSEUM FOR YOU TOO, JACK...

WHAT!?!

...AS THE SPECIAL GUEST OF THE EMPEROR JULIUS CAESAR, THAT IS. HA! HA! HA!

AND THE VERY NEXT DAY...

HA! HA! HA!

WOOF!

CUT HER TITS OFF AND THROW THEM TO THE LIONS!

Who's who in local tele

WHEN WE turn on our TV sets to watch the nightly regional news, we only see the faces of the presenters. How many of us ever stop to wonder about the unseen people working behind the camera? You may be surprised to learn that, just like an iceberg, nine tenths of the regional news team is submerged beneath the surface of the sea. It's two minutes before the programme goes on air. Let's pull back the camera and take a look at who's who in the regional news studio.

1 The Researcher
A junior, though still very important position. Traditionally she must have the silliest name of anyone in the studio. Without the researcher, there would be no-one running round the studio carrying a clipboard and wearing hoopy tights.

2 The Sound Engineer
He must balance the sound levels during the actual broadcast and filter out the sound of the presenter's false teeth clacking before the signal reaches the mixing desk.

3 The Boom Operator
Works in conjunction with the sound engineer and the camera man. It is his job to occasionally dip the microphone in shot just long enough and frequently enough to be distracting. A highly skilled job that requires the ability to point your arms vaguely at whoever is talking.

4 The Sound Mixer
This man takes all the sounds from all the microphones across the studio and balances the levels to produce the final sound that is broadcast. He also has to leave the presenter's microphone switched off for the first 3 seconds of a broadcast, then turn it up far too loud in panic before finally finding the correct level.

5 The Anchorman
He may be just another cog in the Regional News Programme machine, but he is the one that the public sees. As his title suggests, he 'anchors' the programme. Sitting upright with his eyes open and slowly reading things other people have written when he sees a red light go on are just some of the skills he has honed over 35 years in regional broadcasting. Several drink-driving bans and a couple of shoplifting incidents have done tittle to dent his popularity with stupid old women regionwide.

6 Standby Gaffer
Stands on the studio floor It is his job to move out of the way when the camera comes through.

7 Assistant Standby Gaffer
Moves out of the way to allow the standby gaffer to move out of the way of the camera.

8 Local Weatherman
This man must work to very tight deadlines. He has to watch Michael Fish doing the national weather on a portable telly minutes before he goes on air, take the bit relevant to the region and pad it out to about a minute. He will be insanely jealous of the anchorman who can command double his own appearance fee to open carpet warehouse sales etc. The weatherman must als o deliver his piece standing up, and must therefore drink slightly less than the anchorman.

9 Chief Cameraman
In constant contact with the director the cameraman must carefully compose each shot, taking great care to position the camera so that the 'backdrop picture' covers half of the anchorman's face. When the director eventually spots this and informs the cameraman, he must zoom in quickly on the anchorman's ear, allowing the director to cut to camera 2's shot of a bemused looking weatherman picking his nose.

10 Newsreader
The newsreader must have a sense of timing second to none. When his segment is counted in by the director, he must begin reading to the wrong camera for exactly 4 seconds, as demanded by the ISA, before spotting the red light on the other camera. He will probably be in dispute with the station because his grinning, chrome-framed portrait on the foyer wall is smaller than the weatherman's.

11 The News Editor
A time-served journalist, the News editor scans through the national daily tabloids looking for stories with a local interest, which were probably lifted from local weekly rags in the first place. This ensures that every story that makes it on screen is at least four days old. Unsalaried, he is paid a commission of £1 every time the words 'local' or 'region' appear in the script.

12 Best Boy
Runs to the station video library for the Betty Boop cartoons when the anchorman has a stroke on air.

13 Make-up Artist
The harsh lighting in a television studio shows up the smallest imperfections of the skin. So just imagine what it would do to an alcoholic anchorman with cheeks like purple crazy paving and a nose like a baboon with piles's arse. For this reason, the make-up artist is often considered the most important member of the regional programme team, and up to half of the entire production budget can be spent on sufficiently powerful make-up.

14 Post Production Runner
This man must run to the bar and line up the drinks for the Anchorman.

15 Producer
The most important man, after the anchorman, on the studio floor. His job is to open all the doors to allow the anchorman to lumber to the bar immediately after the broadcast

16 Floor Manager
Invariably an aggressive, effeminate Scotsman who's job it is to mince angrily about the studio, bossing everyone around in a patronising voice.

17 The Director
Surely the man who holds the show together. Throughout the show he must sit in the gantry next to a woman who counts backwards whilst looking at tots of television screens.

18 P.A. to Anchorman
A woman who makes sure the anchorman takes his happy pills and explains away his tantrums to the crew. Her other main job is to buy his wife's birthday and anniversary presents. She must also perform a delicate balancing act, allowing him to drink enough before he goes on air so that he doesn't get the shakes, but not so much that he can't focus on the autocue.

If you want to get into local television, there are two recognised routes to take. Firstly, through your father working for the station, or secondly, through your mother working for the station. The following paid staff are all related to the anchorman.

19 Junior Researcher - daughter

20 On-line Producer - son

21 Key Grip - sister's lad

22 Clapper Loader - brother-in-law

23 Foley Artist - niece's husband

24 Rostrum Camera - father

25 Production Assistants - Vera & the kids

First World War Action

The COWARD of COUNTY ICE-CREAM

Flanders. Row upon row of white tombstones, each one telling its own story of courage and tragedy. But at the end of one of these endless rows stands a stone which tells a story which is stranger than fiction itself.

August 4th, 1914, and war fever grips the nation. General Kitchener mounts a campaign to recruit 100,000 soldiers to be killed in the trenches.

BRITAIN NEEDS CANNON FODDER NOW

Have you enlisted, Herbert? They say it'll all be over by Christmas.

No. I'd love to, but somebody has to stay behind and sell ice cream to the women and children.

Over the coming months, Herbert watched and sold ice cream as the men of England packed up their troubles in their old kit bags and marched off to war.

There you are- two Fabs and a Zoom. That's a ha'penny farthing, son.

What would you like, madam?

I'll have a Magnum, please.

Certainly. That's ten bob.

There! That's for you.

Thank you

But Herbert's blood turned as cold as one of his minty stripe choc ices when he unfolded the note.

Gasp!! A white feather!

That night, Herbert gazed at the feather, deep in thought. He knew he had a duty to die for his country, but he also had a duty to his customers. He faced a difficult choice- stay at home and face shame, or go to war and face death.

Hello, Herbert, dear. Did you have a good day selling ice cream?

Yes, my dear. And you? Did you have a good day at the Women's Institute?

Yes, wonderful

I've been talking to Mrs. Wilberforce. Her husband Albert has been gassed in the trenches and had his leg blown off. They've given him a medal. Isn't it marvellous?

Erm... yes, dear

She's so proud

That reminds me, we made this for you at the W.I. craft circle

COWARDY COWARDY CUSTARD

It's true! I AM a coward. The Coward of County Ice Cream

For Herbert, this was the final humiliation. He knew what he had to do.

Two days later, and in the trenches at Ypres there is a brief respite in the relentless gunfire.

Tell you what, Billy. When I get back to Blighty, I'm going to take my girl and buy her the biggest ice cream money can buy

Gaw! Ice cream, eh?

Here she is, look, eating a Walls Choc Top Woppa.

That's what I miss most about back home. Ice cream.

You know, sarge, I can almost hear the van. You know, that tinny, distorted theme from Popeye. It takes me right back.

Hang on a mo. I can hear it too.

And me. And it sounds like it's getting nearer.

The battle weary men peered over the top of their trench and could not believe the sight that met their eyes.

Look! it's Herbert!!

Soon the battlefield at Ypres rang to the sound of Herbert's annoying chimes.

The men lined up for their ice creams. As one fell to the crack of a German shot, another stepped forward to take his place in the queue.

A ninety nine, please, with crushed nuts and monkey's blood

I'll have a blackcurrant split.

After six hours of selling ice cream, Herbert was close to exhaustion.

Jolly good show, old boy! Your plucky ice cream selling has boosted morale no end...

...but I'm afraid you'll have to close your till up now...

...GHQ have sent orders. We're to go over the top just as soon as we've finished our ice creams. Jerry's fire will be pretty heavy, so you'd better get back to Blighty.

And, thank you!

With a heavy heart and a heavy till, Herbert reached inside his pocket for the van key...

...and noticed something flutter to the ground.

Meanwhile...

Right, chaps. Bayonets fixed, gas masks ready, cigarette lighters over hearts...

... and over the top on my whistle.

Suddenly...

It's Herbert! He's driving into no-man's land

Achtung! Einer icenwagen!

Ja! Ja! Schnell

Look! He's distracting the Germans! Quick! Over the top!

Pheeeeep!

Einer neun und neunzig mit minkibluden

Ja! und knacken-nutten, bitte.

Suddenly...

Herbert was killed instantly when his van ran over a mine, but his death was not in vain. His act of bravery allowed the British forces to advance and gain 2 foot 6 inches of mud.

He was buried with full Dairy Produce Industry honours and his name remembered as a hero, and no longer as the Coward of County ice cream.

THE END

Toilets - How they work

THE MODERN toilet is the result of 2,000 years of invention, design and improvement. It is so efficient that we may never pause to consider how it does its miraculous work. So exactly how does a simple push on a lever make our foulage simply vanish?

Amazingly, the secret of the modern flushing lavatory's remarkable performance is hidden away in the big pottery box at the back - which plumbers call a "system". When we pull the lever, a tap is turned on inside the system, causing it to fill up, whilst at the same time, a chemical disc turns the water blue. This blue water is heavier than normal see-through water, and it falls down into the toilet under the force of gravity. The weight of the blue water pushes the excreta and micturant round the S-bend through the main sewer, and safely out onto the beach.

THE TOILET, the loo, the lavatory. call it what you will, we all tak it for granted as an everyday part our lives. But have you ever stoppe to wonder how these technologica

THE T

Toilets in Art

THE MOST famous toilet in art is the Toilet of Venus, the 17th century oil painting by Spanish old master Diego Velazquez, which can be seen at London's National Gallery. But before lavatory lovers get too excited, we should point out that you can't actually see the toilet itself the picture, and Venus had already wiped her arse and laid down on the settee by the time Velazquez started painting her.

Toilets in Pop

FORGET electric guitars, drums and microphones. The toilet has been the most influential instrument in pop music since the 1950s. Every rock'n'roll star from the Rolling Stones, Chuck Berry and the Beatles to Marilyn Manson, Shakin' Stevens and Damon Albarn regularly lock themselves in the toilet in order to evacuate their bowels.

The toilet has affected other rock stars in different ways. King of Rock'n'Roll Elvis Presley died on the toilet whilst straining to pass an enormous stool 9 years after his '68 Comeback Special. Meanwhile Wham! star George Michael was arrested and charged with lewd conduct after waggling his tassel at an undercover policeman in a swanky Beverly Hills public lavatory.

Amazingly, indie band the Kaiser Chiefs find that the toilet is the best place to write their songs. Singer Ricky Wilson told *NME* magazine: "It's not just the best place to write, we find it's the only place where we can come up with new tunes read lyrics. Before we went into the studio to record our new album *The Future is Medieval*, we gorged ourselves on figs, Pontefract Cakes and hot currries made with out-of-date Tandoori prawns. We were pebble-dashing the bowl for a week, and we wrote twenty great new tracks."

arvels of urine and faeces disposal ctually work? It's time to take a eek under the seat and behind he U-bend as we delve into the onderful and mysterious world of...

OILET

Toilets in History

A healthy person goes to the toilet for a number 2 at least 8 times a day, spending more than a quarter of his waking hours ensconced on the pot. So it's not surprising that toilets have played their part at many pivotal moments in history.

If you look carefully at the Bayeux Tapestry, you will see a handle and chain dangling down from the top of William the Conqueror's throne. That's because, at the time of his coronation, the Norman King was really bad with his guts due to the change in the water between France and England. In fact, on the day he was to be crowned, it is said that William woke up with terrible diarrhoea and spent the whole morning sitting on the toilet reading the Domesday Book. As the day wore on, there was no sign of any improvement in the royal bowels and the Archbishop of Canterbury was forced to coronate him right where he sat. Fortunately, the King's elaborate robes covered up the fact that he had his trousers and pants round his ankles, and the heralds' fanfares drowned out most of his farts and plops.

Toilets on Trains

Train toilets have changed a great deal over the years. In the early days of British Rail, the effluent was simply emptied out of the bottom of the toilet and onto the tracks whilst the train was in motion. However, modern environmental concerns coupled with increased passenger numbers mean that such a practice is no longer acceptable. These days, when you pull the flush in a modern Inter-City 125 toilet, instead of emptying onto the tracks, the bangers and mash stays exactly where it is in the bowl, waiting for the next passenger to come along and add another layer.

Toilets in the Future

These days, going to the lavatory can often be a messy and unpleasant business, but all that is set to change as the toilet joins the digital revolution. By the year 2020, anyone who needs to do a duty will simply have to connect their fundament up to a computer via a USB cable. The stools will then be downloaded onto your hard drive in a convenient "MP3No.2" format, showing up on the desktop as a little brown sausage-shaped icon surrounded by flies. It will be a simple matter to use the mouse to click and drag this into your toilet folder, before selecting "Flush" from the drop-down menu. Clean, simple, completely paperless... and no need to wash your hands!

Next Week:

Read & Learn & Look & Read & Wonder & Learn -

Dr Robert Chartham's **Ring of Pubis**

THE JIMMY SAVILE STORY

THE PIRATES OF PLYMOUTH ARGYLE

IN 1751, TIRED OF LANGUISHING IN THE DOLDRUMS OF LEAGUE DIVISION 1, THE ENTIRE PLYMOUTH ARGYLE FOOTBALL TEAM SWAPPED PROFESSIONAL SOCCER FOR A LIFE ON THE OCEAN WAVES ABOARD THE PIRATE SHIP THE JOLLY PILGRIM. LED BY THEIR BLOODTHIRSTY CAPTAIN RON REDBEARD, IT WASN'T LONG BEFORE TALES OF THE FOOTBALLING CUT-THROATS' EXPLOITS SPREAD FAR AND WIDE. BY THE MIDDLE YEARS OF THE 18TH CENTURY, PLYMOUTH ARGYLE FC WERE THE MOST FEARED BAND OF BUCCANEERS ON THE HIGH SEAS.

AVAST, ME HEARTIES. KEEP IT TIGHT AT THE BACK. LAST FIVE MINUTES...

MAN ON, MR HAYLES!

AH-HAAR! 'TIS REAL PROW TO STERN STUFF, MR KEMP! BUT WE'VE PROVED THE BETTER SIDE OVER THE NINETY MINUTES.

AYE, CAP'N. THE OTHER CREW MUST BE AS SICK AS YOUR PARROT.

PHEEP!

HOORAY! 'TIS ALL OVER! WELL BATTLED, ME SALTY SEA DOGS!

THERE'LL BE DANCING ON THE DECKS OF THE JOLLY PILGRIM TONIGHT.

FIVE MINUTES LATER.

DAMN YOU, SIR. YOU'LL ANSWER TO HIS MAJESTY'S NAVY AND TO FIFA FOR THIS.

AH-HAAR! 'TIS RELEGATION TO DAVY JONES LOCKER FOR YOU, YE SCURVY SWABS!

THE PIRATES CELEBRATED THEIR VICTORY WELL INTO THE NIGHT.

'TWAS A FINE WIN TODAY. THE WHOLE CREW SHOWED TREMENDOUS STRENGTH IN DEPTH.

AAR! 'TWAS A BATTLE OF TWO HALVES TO BE SURE, CAP'N

AYE! WE SET OUR STALLS OUT EARLY DOORS WHEN WE BLASTED THEM AMIDSHIPS.

NO DISRESPECT TO THE LADS OF THE GULL, BUT WE'VE COME UP AGAINST MANY A MORE FEARSOME RABBLE THAN THEM...

AND AT THE END OF THE DAY, WE SLIT THEIR YELLOW BELLIED GIZZARDS!

STRIKE UP THE SQUEEZE BOX, MR NALIS.

AYE-AYE, CAP'N!

WE'LL SING A SHANTY TO CELEBRATE OUR VICTORY.

THE JOLLY PILGRIM DREW ALONGSIDE THE GRECIAN. THE BATTLE WAS ABOUT TO COMMENCE.

PHEEEP!

AAARGH!

HA-AAAR!

TASTE PLYMOUTH ARGYLE STEEL, YE LILLY-LIVERED SEA DOG!

AAARGH!

'TIS A SOLID START FROM OUR LADS, CAP'N.

THAT IT IS, MR KEMP. THAT IT IS.

THE BATTLE RAGED FOR 89 MINUTES.

THESE SQUID-SUCKING CURS ARE GIVING AS GOOD AS THEY GET. WE STILL HAVEN'T MANAGED TO GET THEIR TREASURE.

AYE, CAP'N. THE MEN OF THE GRECIAN ARE NO WALKOVERS, FOR SURE. YOU COULDN'T PUT A CIGARETTE PARCHMENT BETWEEN THE TWO CREWS.

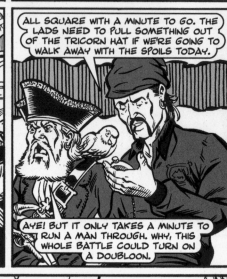

ALL SQUARE WITH A MINUTE TO GO. THE LADS NEED TO PULL SOMETHING OUT OF THE TRICORN HAT IF WE'RE GOING TO WALK AWAY WITH THE SPOILS TODAY.

AYE! BUT IT ONLY TAKES A MINUTE TO RUN A MAN THROUGH. WHY, THIS WHOLE BATTLE COULD TURN ON A DOUBLOON.

SUDDENLY...

AAAARGH!

BREACH ME HULL, BUZSAKY'S GONE DOWN! OUR CREATIVE MIDSHIPS DYNAMO CROCKED AT THIS CRUCIAL STAGE OF THE ENGAGEMENT.

DID I NOT WANT TO HEAR THAT PIECE OF NEWS?

ARRRGH! MY KNEE! BY NEPTUNE, IT HURTS. IT HURTS BAD!

STEADY MR BUZSAKY. LET'S HAVE A LOOK.

'TIS YOUR CRUCIATE LIGAMENT, MR BUZSAKY. I'M AFRAID YOU'LL BE OUT FOR THE REST OF THE SEASON.

DO WE HAVE ANY SUBSTITUTES, MR KEMP?

NO, CAP'N. ALL THE RESERVES ARE DOWN WITH THE SCURVY.

THEN WE'LL HAVE TO FIGHT THE LAST TEN MINUTES WITH TEN SOULS. IF WE CAN DROP BACK AND SHUT UP SHOP, WE MIGHT JUST COME OUT OF THIS WITH HONOURS EVEN.

I'LL FIGHT, CAP'N. LET ME GO ON AND FIGHT!

WHAT!?! YOU!?! YOU'RE NOUGHT BUT A CABIN BOY!

BUT I'VE WATCHED THEM FIGHT, CAPTAIN. JUST GIVE ME THE CHANCE AND I'LL SHOW YOU WHAT I CAN DO. I WON'T LET YOU DOWN. I'LL GIVE 100%

HMM! I DON'T KNOW...

The Viz Careers Officer

ONLY a few people live the glamorous, jet-set life of an international megastar; a dizzying, non-stop merry-go-round of glittering Hollywood premieres, Caribbean sailing holidays and photoshoots for the glossy pages of *Hello!* magazine. It is a world the rest of us can only imagine in our wildest dreams. But for every A-lister like BEYONCE, MADONNA and JONNY DEPP, there are countless thousands of D-listers like KERRY KATONA, BUBBLE out of *Big Brother 2* and JOE SWASH. These celebrity also-rans live their lives on the fringes of fame, desperately craning their necks to get a small share of the spotlight at a showbiz party or a couple of sentences in a downmarket tabloid gossip column.

And with an ever-increasing number of low-budget TV channels broadcasting countless hours of pointless reality shows, demand for D-listers has never been higher. A life in the semi-sparkly suburbs of stardom is an increasingly popular career choice for the school leaver who perhaps didn't do very in their GCSEs. But what exactly does it take the reach the foggy foothills of celebrity? Let's look at the working lives of these dimly glowing stars in the showbiz firmament...

So you want to be a D-LIST CELEBRITY?

THE PUBLIC has an insatiable appetite for information about celebrities. A trip to any high street bookshop will reveal shelf upon shelf of best-selling autobiographies written by stars of stage and screen. But pop round the corner to your local Home Bargains store and there, amongst the cheap sellotape, out-of-date diaries and Arabic Toblerone, you will find the D-list celebrity memoirs piled high. As a D-list celebrity, you will be expected to produce one of these spaciously-typeset and generously-illustrated volumes every six months or so. Producing an autobiography can be a time-consuming business, and could easily involve up to half-a-dozen ten-minute phonecalls to your ghost writer.

THE media has an endless fascination with the weights of D-list celebrities, so part of your job will be to fluctuate wildly between unhealthily obese and dangerously thin. Remember, if you're somewhere in between those two extremes, the papers will lose interest in you and your days as a D-lister will be numbered. It's a good idea to put on a few stone before going on a crash diet to make the contrast more impressive in the 'Before' and 'After' pictures of you on the beach that will undoubtedly get printed in *Hot Stars* magazine. The secret behind your fab new look will most likely get you 4 minutes on the GMTV sofa with Andrew Castle and Emma Crosby, discussing your hastily-produced diet & workout DVD, which will already be piled up in pound-shop bargain bins by the time Lorraine Kelly comes on.

FOR A D-list celebrity, publicity is like oxygen; without it, your career will literally shrivel and die. The public is fickle and will quickly forget any celebrity who falls out of view, so you must be prepared to do everything and anything to stay in the limelight. Whilst real stars such as Clint Eastwood and Meryl Streep can pick and choose their next film project and David Bowie can spend ten years working on his next album, as a D-lister you must be prepared to cheerfully accept humiliations that you wouldn't be expected to put up with in Guantanamo Bay. Here we see a typical modern celebrity having his turds sniffed, poked and sneered at by Gillian McKeith in order to get on television.

PRODUCT endorsement is a popular sideline for all celebrities. Not only is advertising work extremely lucrative, but more importantly it keeps your all-too-forgettable face fresh in the public's mind. But whilst top stars like Sting, Jennifer Aniston and David Beckham earn a pretty penny endorsing prestige products like Jaguar cars, l'Oreal cosmetics and Gillette razors, as a D-lister your choice is a bit more limited. You will more likely be called upon to lend your name and face to adverts for plastic double glazing, cheap pastie shops or downmarket frozen food stores.

LIVING your life in the 15 watt glare of D-list publicity, it is important to have an expert in charge of your PR. It is their job to come up with a series of news-management strategies to keep the tabloids and gossip rags fed with a constant stream of inconsequential tittle-tattle about their clients. A typical celebrity's month might see them getting their partner's name tattooed on their neck, declaring themselves bankrupt, renewing their vows on a tropical beach, slurring their words on a daytime TV chat-show, dumping their partner via text message, going into re-hab after becoming addicted to painkillers and getting the tattoo of their former partner's name lasered off their neck. As a D-lister, these stories cement your reputation as a celebrity in the public consciousness, and create a smokescreen that obscures the fact that you don't actually do anything.

IF YOU'RE looking for a Monday-to-Friday 9-to-5 job, then a career as a D-list celebrity is not for you. Late nights come with the territory; at least a couple of times a week you'll want to be pictured in the paper coming out of a club in the wee small hours. And whilst a genuine star like Scarlett Johansson can get the paps flashing by simply turning up, as a lesser celeb you'll have to work a little bit harder to grab your 15 seconds of not-quite-fame. For a D-lister, there are a number of tried-and-tested strategies you can try to get the lenses pointing in your direction. If you're a lady, a short skirt that reveals an expanse of upper-thigh cellulite can be enough to earn you a priceless third of a page in *Heat* magazine. On the other hand, removing your knickers in the night-club toilets before climbing into your cab in an artfully careless fashion can see you pictured in the *Daily Star*'s *Goss* page with an 'Oops!' flash superimposed over your minge. Male D-listers may like to get into a scuffle with lensmen or simply punch their taxi driver. Both of these techniques have the added advantage of serving up a further burst of publicity when your assault case comes to court in a couple of months' time.

NEXT WEEK: SO YOU WANT TO BE A MONK?

DAVID BLAINE
STALAG MAGICIAN

THE GERMAN ADVANCE IN THE ARDENNES CATCHES THE ALLIES BY SURPRISE AND NETS THOUSANDS OF PRISONERS, AMONG THEM CAPTAIN DAVID BLAINE, THE RENOWNED ESCAPOLOGIST AND LIGHT ENTERTAINER. HE IS TRANSPORTED TO THE NOTORIOUS STALAG 13 CAMP, FROM WHICH- AS YET- NO POW HAS LEFT ALIVE...

THIS BLAINE CHARACTER IS RED HOT, ACCORDING TO GEN FROM H.Q. BEATS ME HOW THEY MANAGED TO NAB HIM AT ALL...

SUPRISED HIM SITTING UP A TWENTY FOOT POLE AT A TROOP SHOW, SIR. AUDIENCE AND CONCERT PARTY BUGGERED OFF PDQ.

BLAINE HELD OUT FOR A MONTH BUT HAD TO COME DOWN EVENTUALLY- CALL OF NATURE.

PLEASED TO MEET YOU, MAJOR.

GASP! DER PRISONER HAS ESCAPED HIS HANDCUFFS!

HO HO! LET THE GAMES BEGIN, EH, BLAINE!

SILENCE! THERE WILL BE NO GAMES!

WELCOME TO STALAG 13, BLAINE.

UNLUCKY FOR SOME, MAJOR.

THE NEXT DAY...

I RETURN TONIGHT. YOU ARE IN CHARGE, SCMIDT.

IF BLAINE ESCAPES, YOU VILL TAKE HIS PLACE

MEIN GOTT! WASS IS DAS?!

OUR BLAINE HAS BEEN BUSY. GRAF'S CAR'S A MUD PIE!

HO HO! HE MUST BE BUILDING A BALLY TUNNEL ALREADY!

SILENCE! SCHMIDT! SHOOT A PRISONER!

JAWOHL, GENERAL!

MY GOD, MAN! YOU CAN'T DO THAT!

MY DEAR MAJOR, THERE IS NUSSING I CANNOT DO.

AS NIGHT FALLS...

COAST CLEAR, BROWN. BETTER WAKE BLAINE, FIND OUT ABOUT THIS TUNNEL OF HIS.

POOR CHAP! SEEMS A SHAME TO WAKE HIM.

GREAT SCOTT, MAJOR, LOOK!

WHAT THE!!...

THREE DAYS, BROWN. I THINK WE CAN SAFELY SAY THAT BLAINE HAS MADE IT. HERE'S TO A DAMN FINE JOB!

I'LL DRINK TO THAT. SHAME HE COULDN'T STICK AROUND LONGER. HE COULD HAVE TAUGHT US A LOT.

BLAINE!

BOURBON CREAMS, MAJOR, QUICKLY!

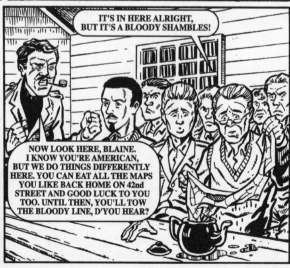

YOU are Dr. MIRIAM STOPPARD the REF!

Test *your* knowledge of footballers' problems. What would *you* do in this situation if *you* were *Dr. Miriam Stoppard the Ref?*

DURING a match, the ball is knocked into touch by a member of the attacking side. As the throw-in is taken, an opposing defender approaches you on the edge of the 18 yard box and confides that he is having trouble maintaining an erection.

He is 21 years old, his partner is 23. She is very understanding, but it is causing tension in their relationship and he fears she may start to look elsewhere for sexual fulfilment. *What do you do?*

a. *Suggest he asks his GP for a course of vaso-dilatory drugs to increase blood flow in his penis.*

b. *Tell him to relax, and experiment with non penetrative forms of sex.*

c. *Stop the game and award an indirect free kick against the defending side.*

The correct answer is b. The commonest cause of erectile disfunction amongst footballers is stress. Worrying about the problem will only make it worse. If he can relax with other forms of sex play, his mind will be taken off the problem and nine times out of ten, the condition will vanish of its own accord.

AS THE GERMAN TOOK CONTROL OF THE DESPATCH RIDER'S BIKE, BARON VON RICHTHOFEN EXPLAINED THE PLOT.

HA! VEN ZE FAKE LETTERS ARE PUT UP ZE CHIMNEY, ZE BRITISH TROOPS VILL GET ZE SOCKS, ZE HANKIES, ZE AFTERSHAVE UNT ZE WH SCHMIDT TOKENS...

...ZEY VILL BE SO DISAPPOINTED, ZEY VILL LOSE ZE VILL TO VIN VORLD VOR VUN!

IN NO TIME AT ALL, THE DOPPELGANGER ARRIVED AT THE BRITISH HQ...

...AND HIS PERFECT ENGLISH AROUSED NO SUSPICIONS AT THE GATE.

WOTCHER, COCK! WOT 'AVE YOU GOT THERE THEN?

GAW! IT'S THE LETTERS FOR SANTA, OLD CHAP!

LAVERLY! BRING 'EM IN. THE FIELD MARSHALL IS WAITING, ME OLD CHINA PLATE.

LETTERS FOR SANTA, SIR

SPLENDID, SPLENDID! GOOD SHOW!

TOP HOLE, MY MAN. I'LL GET THESE BLIGHTERS UP THE CHIMNEY. YOU GET YOURSELF A NICE CUP OF TEA, WHAT?

YES, SIR.

SO...

I SAY!

WHAT THE?!...

GREAT SCOTT! HE PUSHED IN... HE PUSHED RIGHT TO THE FRONT!!

GET DOWN, EVERYONE! HE'S A BALLY BOSCH!!

TAKE THAT, YOU SQUAREHEAD!

AIIEEE!!

WHAT'S GOING ON?

LOOK AT THESE GIFT REQUESTS. SOAP ON A ROPE... BATH SALTS... NOVELTY TIES... AN ANDY CAPP OMNIBUS...

THESE LETTERS ARE FAKES!

THE BRAVEST PONY OF THEM ALL

SUMMER 1916, AND EUROPE WAS IN THE GRIP OF WAR. IN THE FIELDS OF NORTHERN FRANCE, THE BRITISH AND GERMAN ARMIES HAD BEEN LOCKED IN A BLOODY STALEMATE FOR THE LAST TWO YEARS, LEAVING COUNTLESS THOUSANDS OF DEAD AND MAIMED. BUT THE HORRORS OF THE SOMME WERE THE FURTHEST THING FROM THE MIND OF YOUNG WILTSHIRE FARMER'S DAUGHTER BUNTY TWINKLE, AS SHE RODE HER PONY MUFFIN TO VICTORY IN THE VILLAGE GYMKHANA.

WELL DONE, MUFFIN!

ANOTHER CLEAR ROUND!

BUNTY WAS BURSTING WITH PRIDE AS SHE RECEIVED HER ROSETTE FROM THE MAYOR.

CONGRATULATIONS, YOUNG LADY.

THANK YOU, YOUR WORSHIP!

SUDDENLY, A MILITARY-LOOKING MAN STOOD FORWARD AND SPOKE.

THAT'S A FINE PONY YOU HAVE THERE, MISS.

THANK YOU. HE'S ALWAYS IN RIBBONS.

ALLOW ME TO INTRODUCE MYSELF. I'M COLONEL BROOKES-WARD, OF THE KING'S OWN WILTSHIRE MOUNTED ARTILLERY, AND I'VE GOT A SPECIAL JOB FOR MUFFIN...

...IN FRANCE!

YOU SEE, THE GERMANS HAVE ERECTED A SERIES OF FENCES ACROSS THE SOMME, AND WE NEED A HORSE THAT CAN JUMP OVER THEM TO DELIVER A SET OF ORDERS TO AN ADVANCE BATTALION AT THE FRONT LINE.

BUT I CAN'T POSSIBLY LET HIM GO, COLONEL.

YOU SEE, WE'RE COMPETING IN A PONY CLUB POINT-TO-POINT JUST OUTSIDE DEVIZES NEXT WEEK.

I'M SORRY, MISS. BUT MUFFIN HAS BEEN CONSCRIPTED INTO HIS MAJESTY'S ARMY AND HE'LL BE ON THE BOAT TO FRANCE THIS VERY EVENING.

WELL, IF HE GOES, THEN SO SHALL I!

I CAN'T ALLOW THAT, BUNTY. THE BATTLEFIELDS OF NORTHERN FRANCE ARE A SCENE OF SLAUGHTER, DEATH AND DISEASE ON AN UNIMAGINABLE SCALE. IT'S NO PLACE FOR TWELVE YEAR OLD GIRL.

BUT MUFFIN WON'T LET ANYONE ELSE RIDE HIM BUT ME, COLONEL.

NONSENSE. I'VE BROKEN MORE HORSES THAN YOU'VE HAD HOT DINNERS, YOUNG LADY. I'M QUITE SURE I CAN RIDE YOUR PONY.

NOW STAND ASIDE.

WOOOAAAH!

ATTA BOY!

HMM! YOUR PONY CERTAINLY HAS SPIRIT, BUNTY. AND YOU'RE CLEARLY THE ONLY ONE HE'LL ALLOW TO SIT ON HIS BACK.

VERY WELL, YOU SHALL COME TO FRANCE WITH HIM. YOU'RE THE ONLY CHANCE WE'VE GOT TO GET THOSE VITAL ORDERS THROUGH TO THE FRONT LINE.

DID YOU HEAR THAT, MUFFIN? I'M COMING WITH YOU TO THE WAR! WHAT AN ADVENTURE!

BARELY SIX HOURS LATER, BUNTY AND MUFFIN WERE ON THE DECK OF A TROOPSHIP BOUND FOR DIEPPE.

THERE GOES THE LAST OF ENGLAND, MUFFIN. WILL WE EVER SEE HER AGAIN?

THE VERY NEXT DAY, THE PAIR ARRIVED AT THE BRITISH ARMY HQ AT BAZENTIN LE PETIT.

YOU SEE, THE BOSCHE HAVE PUT BARRIERS UP HERE, HERE, HERE, HERE AND HERE.

INCLUDING VERTICALS, A COMBINATION, A CROSS-RAIL, A WATER-JUMP, AN OXER...

AND FINALLY A HOG'S BACK HERE, JUST BY THE FORWARD POSITION WHERE MY MEN ARE AWAITING THEIR ORDERS.

THOSE FENCES WILL BE NO PROBLEM FOR MUFFIN. HE'S BEEN PUISSANCE CHAMPION AT THE CHIPPENHAM PONY CLUB MEET FOR THE PAST THREE YEARS RUNNING.

HE NEVER REFUSES A JUMP.

THIS WILL BE THE MOST IMPORTANT CLEAR ROUND OF HIS LIFE. HE CAN'T AFFORD TO SLIP UP, EVEN ONCE.

SURELY HE'LL BE ALLOWED FOUR FAULTS, THOUGH, PROVIDED HE MAKES UP THE LOST TIME IN THE FINAL GALLOP FOR THE FRONT LINE...?

I'M AFRAID NOT.

THE BEASTLY HUN HAVE BOOBY-TRAPPED THE FENCES.

IF MUFFIN KNOCKS DOWN A POLE, YOU'LL BOTH BE BLOWN TO KINGDOM COME!

GASP!

HERE ARE THE ORDERS, BUNTY. GUARD THEM WITH YOUR LIFE.

DON'T WORRY, COLONEL. MUFFIN WON'T LET YOU DOWN.

GOD SPEED.

DING-A-LING!

GIDDY-UP MUFFIN!

COME ON, BOY. JUMP LIKE YOU'VE NEVER JUMPED BEFORE.

BUNTY AND MUFFIN ARE OFF TO A CONFIDENT START. THEY'VE CLEARED THE FIRST OBSTACLE WITH EASE!

THEY'RE CUTTING IT TIGHT TO THE SECOND FENCE!

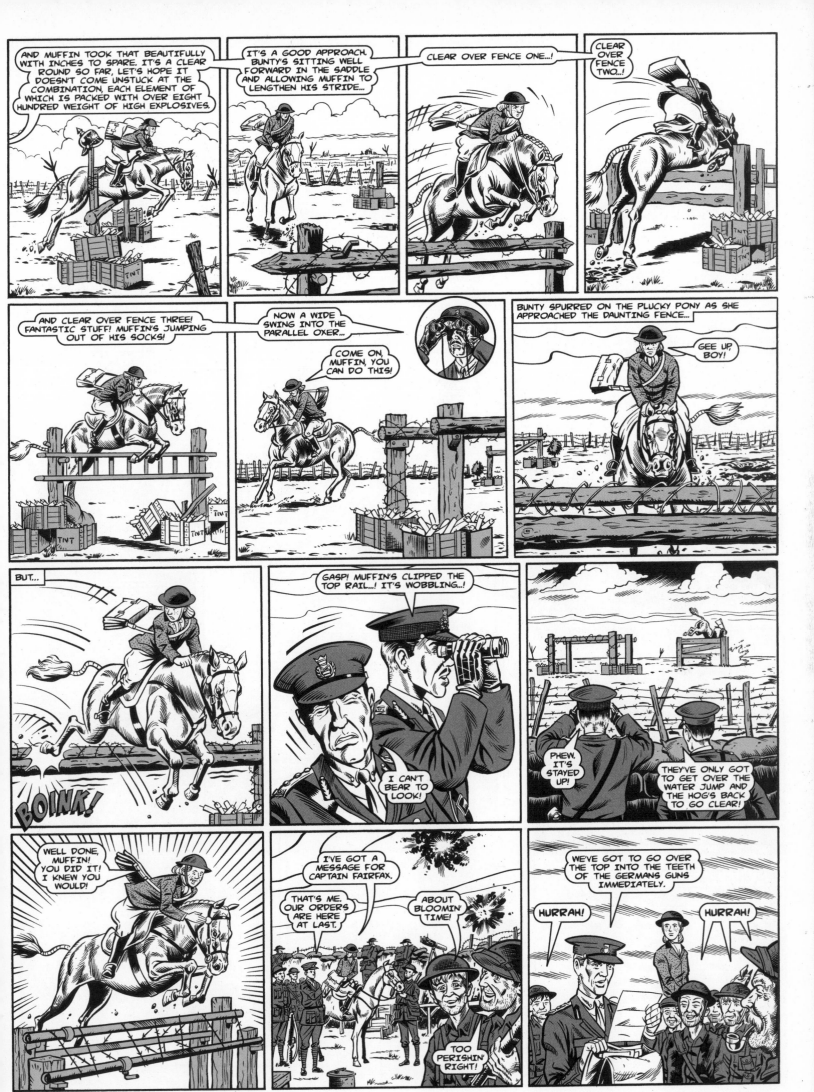

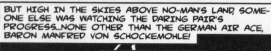

JACK BLACK AND THE CHICKEN MYSTERY

THE CHINESE NEW YEAR HOLIDAYS WERE HERE AGAIN, AND BOY SLEUTH JACK BLACK, AND HIS DOG DETECTIVE SILVER, WERE STAYING WITH HIS AUNT MEG IN HER CONVERTED PIT HEAD WINDING HOUSE IN THE TINY WELSH VILLAGE OF LLANGOGOGOGOGOCH.

Test YOUR Circus Funnyman Knowledge~
YOU are the Clown

You are standing on one side of the ring when your colleague drives in in a small car. Suddenly, the doors fall off and a lot of white smoke comes from under the bonnet. He approaches and asks you to look under the bonnet. What do you do?

Answer ~ You should refuse to do as requested several times. Eventually, you give in to your colleague's request, lift the bonnet and press the hidden button that squirts the water out of the radiator into your face.

Half way through the second half of a show you are on a stepladder sticking wallpaper onto a wooden partition wall in the centre of the ring. Suddenly, the ringmaster appears and tells you very publicly to leave the ring as you are making too much mess. How do you respond?

Answer ~ The correct course of action is to come down from the ladder with the paste bucket and chase the ringmaster several times around the ring. Wait for him to stop and duck before throwing the bucketful of confetti over the audience.

You find yourself sitting in your dressing room with a stinking hangover when you suddenly realise that you are 60- years old, have no money put by, and are living in a series of muddy fields. It also dawns on you that nobody actually enjoys watching your show, and that you merely fill in time whilst the good acts prepare their equipment. What do you do?

Answer ~ In this situation you should down another bottle of Netto own brand whisky before putting your head in the CalorGas oven in your caravan.

215

ASK anyone to name their favourite inventions for keeping food cool in the kitchen, and chances are that somewhere in their list they'll name the fridge. The fridge, or to give it its technical name 'The Refrigerator' is a miracle of engineering that ranks alongside the wheel, the microchip and the Ronco Buttoneer in the pantheon of scientific progress. We all take our fridges for granted as they sit humming away in our kitchens, hard at work keeping our food cold around the clock. But have you ever stopped for a moment to think what's inside your fridge? Let's open the door and shed some light on this mysterious marvel of our age. It's time to Read and Look and Wonder and Learn as we take a peek inside...

THE

Mu

1 The shelves

It is often said that the shelves are the backbone of a refrigerator. Without them, food would have to be stored on the bottom of the fridge in a big pile. With them, we can keep our raw and prepared foods safely separated, thus preventing the transfer of harmful bacteria. However, as with many innovations, fridge shelves have also been used for evil purposes. US cannibal Jeffrey Dahmer used the shelves in his fridge to keep the uncooked heads of his victims separate from their cooked hands and genitals, and as a result the Milwaukee monster never suffered from food poisoning throughout his murderous spree.

Rind
(not always present)

Hole
(not always present)

Cheese

2 The salad drawer

Before the invention of the salad drawer, a typical bag of lettuce bought from the supermarket would only last for a week in the fridge before it turned brown and had to be thrown away. Thanks to this marvellous technological innovation, the same bag can be stored for up to three times as long before you throw it away.

3 The cheese compartment

Cheese is possibly one of the fascinating things you will find in your fridge. This yellow foodstuff is so important that it merits its own designated compartment in the top of the fridge door. If we take a cross-section through a typical piece of cheese, we can see that it is sometimes full of holes, though sometimes it is not. Popular types of cheese include mature cheddar, mild cheddar, brie, babybel, dairylea and ready-grated.

How it Works

This is where things get a little technical, so girls should skip this bit - perhaps go and help mum make a cup of tea!
Your fridge uses electricity to keep things cold. Amazingly, it is exactly the same sort of electricity that your microwave oven uses to make things hot. So how does it work? 240 volts go into the back of the fridge, where some humming occurs intermittently, causing the fridge to go cold. Simple but brilliant!

A busy mum shows her children the modern refrigerator her husband has bought for her.

4 The egg rack

One of the most fami
features of the fridge is the egg ra
in the door. For the UK market, i
designed to accommodate a doz
standard hen's eggs, but tra
around the world and it's a differ
story. The pygmies of the Belg
Congo have tiny racks to suit
humming bird eggs which they ha
for breakfast, whereas the fridg
belonging to the Masai tribespeo
of the African Veldt have great
racks adapted for ostrich egg
But one thing remains the sa
wherever you are. No matter w
size our egg rack, none of us u
them because we simply put
egg box on the shelves.

RIDGE

Best Friend in the Kitchen

Fridges ~ Past and Future

The earliest fridge discovered by archaeologists was found in 1926 by grave robber Howard Carter in the tomb of the Egyptian boy king Tutankhamen. When the 4000-year-old solid gold fridge was opened, it was found to contain mummified cheese, bacon, sausages and milk, all intended to provide sustenance for the dead Pharaoh on his journey to the afterlife. When strange heiroglyphs on the side of each item were translated by British Museum Egyptologists, they turned out to read 'Best before the Dynasty of the Sun King Amenhotep III'. Consequently, Carter had to throw them all in the bin.

Today's fridges reach temperatures of around 2 or 3 degrees centigrade, sufficient to stop sausages going off for about a week. But scientists at Berlin's Zanussi Institute are already working on an atomic powered super-fridge that will be able to reach a temperature of -273°c, or absolute zero. Sausages kept in this fridge would still be okay for around 500 million years, longer than the expected life of the Earth! One drawback, however, is that at this temperature the speed of light approaches zero. So when the busy mum of 2020 opens her fridge door and the light comes on, it could be hours before she can see where anything is.

6 **The freezer compartment**
This is the coldest part of the fridge, and it is where we keep our frozen food, such as pizzas, turkey dinosaurs and fish fingers. But you may be surprised to learn that not all fridges are equipped with freezer compartments. Above the Arctic Circle, the Inuit people keep their milk, sausages and cheese in their fridge just like everyone else, but they keep frozen food in the snow outside their igloo doors, where the temperature never rises above minus 30° centigrade. Contrary to what you might expect, polar bears rarely steal this food, as they have no way of cooking it.

5 **The light**
This ingenious device allows us to see what is in our fridge. We all know that it comes on when we open the door, but the question that has been asked for generations is: does the light go off when we close the door? In truth, it is a conundrum that has occupied scientists for years, and the answer is, they simply don't know. Like Fermat's Last Theorem for mathematicians, solving the so-called Fridge Light Hypothesis is the Holy Grail for refrigerator boffins. Indeed, since 1922 the Hotpoint Foundation has offered a prize of $1million for any scientist who can prove definitively whether or not the light goes out when the fridge door is shut. To date, the prize remains unclaimed.

NEXT ISSUE in Read & Look & Wonder & Learn: We take a fascinating look at what goes on in the exciting world of a Chicken Processing Plant

SAINT MICHAEL, THE PATRON SAINT OF UNDERPANTS

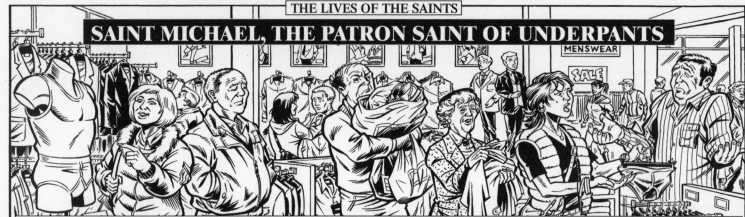

ASK ANY MAN in the street where he buys his underpants and he'll probably say he doesn't know as his wife or his mum buys them for him. Ask his wife or his mum where she buys them, and she'll probably say Marks and Spencers. The high street store's St. Michael brand underpants are as much a part of British life as double-decker buses, Big Ben and boiled beef & carrots. But have you ever stopped to wonder who Saint Michael was, and why his name is inextricably linked to your nether garments? Here's the story of one of our most endearing Saints...

1. MICHAEL was born over 2000 years ago on the outskirts of Rome. His father died when he was very small and his mother was forced to work as humble laundry woman at the Colosseum. It was her task to wash the Christians' underpants after a show, before taking them to the local charity shop. As a boy, Michael would spend many hours watching his mother scrubbing the soiled gussets on the banks of the Tigris. "Underpant cleanliness is next to Godliness," she would often say, and it is a lesson he would never forget.

2. WHEN he became a man, Michael travelled to Galilee to take part in a census that had been ordered by the Roman Emperor Caligula. On the road, he came across a Pharisee who had been waylaid by robbers who had stripped him naked and left him for dead. Despite the man's cries, many people had walked past on the other side. But Michael, taking pity on him, decided to do what he could to help. Removing his own pants, he gave them to the man. "God Bless you," said the Pharisee. "I was naked, but you gave me your pants."

3. THAT night as he slept, he was visited by an Angel of the Lord. Michael was afraid, but the Angel calmed his fears. "Michael," he said. "You have pleased the Lord with your charity, and He has chosen you to do His bidding. From this day you must travel the land, helping those who are vexed with their undergarments." The next morning, Michael dismissed his vision as merely a dream. But then he found a pair of brand new 60% cotton underpants in a bush to replace the ones he had given the Pharisee, and he knew the Lord had spoken.

4. MICHAEL went on. In a village he came across Tibothy of Aramethea who was crippled and had not walked for many years. He told Michael that he had bought a pair of pants that were too small, and they were cutting off the circulation to his legs. "Why has the Lord forsaken me?" cried Tibothy. Michael laid his hands upon Tibothy's pants and they started to grow. Tibothy looked at the size label on the waistband. "It is a miracle," he cried." These pants were once small and made me lame, yet now they are medium and I can walk."

5. IN THE next village, Michael came upon a wedding. There was much rejoicing and feasting, but one man was sitting apart from everyone with his pants in a sack of rude cloth. Michael sought him out. "Brother, what vexes you?" he asked. The man told him that he had eaten a full packet of Smints without reading the warning on the box. He had then sneezed and soiled his shreddies. Michael placed his hand upon the bag. "Go and rejoin the party, your pants are clean," he said. And when he looked, he saw his pants were lemon fresh.

6. ONE day, Michael came to the town of Giddeon, which is called Belhaboneb and found it besieged by the Bathshebalites. The leader of the attacking army offered to call a truce if any citizen of the town could defeat his champion, a giant called Goliath. No one dared take up the challenge. Then, Michael stepped forward. The Bathshebalites laughed as Michael calmly took off his trolleys. Selecting a small rock, he put it on the elasticated waistband, stretched it back and fired it. It struck Goliath between the eyes, felling him in an instant.

7. ONCE, he came upon a man in the street who had been knocked over by a Roman chariot. Even though he was badly injured, he was refusing to see a physician to have his wounds tended. "I have neglected to take my mother's advice, and this morning I put on a old pair of pants which were full of holes," he told Michael. "And great will be my embarrassment if the physician sees the state of them." Michael smiled. "Go forth and seek the physician," he said. The man stood up and looked up his toga, and lo, the holes in his pants were gone.

8. NEWS of Michael's deeds spread quickly, and soon he found that wherever he went he was greeted by crowds. Damascus was troubled with storms, and a multitude whose pants had blown off their washing lines came to him. "Help us," they cried. "We have no pants." Michael brought forth two bed sheets and five yards of elastic and told them, "Go and make underpants." Amazingly, they were able to make 5000 pairs, enough for everyone. "It's a miracle," they cried. "Our parts of shame were cold, but now they are nice and panted."

9. AT THIS time, word of Michael's miracles also reached the Emperor Caligula. He was a cruel leader, and he had recently tried to launch his own range of kinky Roman posing pouches and G-strings. News that a man was performing miracles on old, damaged and worn-out underpants made him very angry and he decided to put a stop to his actions. "Bring me this man who calls himself Michael," he told his Praetorian Guard. "Let him answer to Caesar for his actions." The guards immediately went out to look for Michael.

10. BY NOW, Michael had gathered around him a band of loyal followers who would question him about the ways of pants. But one of their number, Primarcus, was jealous of Michael's fame and envious of his abilities to perform miracles with shreddies. When one of the Praetorian Guards approached him and asked him to identify the one who was called Michael, Primarcus said he would. It was agreed that the following night, the traitor would bring the group to the town square and indicate which was Michael by giving him a wedgie.

11. THE following night during tea, Michael addressed his followers. "This evening, one of you here will betray me with a wedgie," he said. They all looked shocked. "No, Michael," they cried. "We shall never betray you." But later that night in the town square, Primarcus did as he had promised. He stepped forward, kissed Michael on both cheeks and then pulled his bills right up his crack for all to see. Michael's eyes watered at the betrayal. He was put in chains and led away to answer to the Emperor.

12. MICHAEL was brought before Caesar. The angry Emperor accused him of ruining sales of his own range of impractical underwear. But he said he would show mercy and spare Michael's life if he promised to stop performing miracles on people's pants. Michael told him that he could not make that promise, as he had been commanded by God to go throughout the land caring for the grundies of those in need. "It would be easier for a camel to pass through the tassel flap of some Y-fronts than for me to disobey the Lord," he said.

13. CALIGULA sentenced Michael to death, and he was taken to Rome to face the lions in the Colosseum. As the ravenous beasts circled, Michael showed no fear and his pants remained unshitted. "I do not fear death. I fear nothing but the judgement of the Lord," he cried. Awed by his bravery, the crowd's bloodthirsty jeers subsided, replaced by a respectful silence. After five minutes in the arena, all that was left lying in the sand was Michael's pants, as unsoiled as the moment he put them on that morning.

14. MICHAEL was canonised and made Patron Saint of Underpants in 1327 by Pope Innocent IV. His own Y-fronts, taken from the arena after his martyrdom, have rested ever since in the Cathedral in Istanbul, housed in a reliquary shaped like a wicker laundry basked. Legend has it that if ever skidmata appear on the gusset, then the day of judgement is at hand. In an age-old ceremony, every ten years the Archbishop of Constantinople removes the pants from their reliquary, turns them inside out and gives them a quick sniff.

Next Week ~ Saint John-Stevas, Patron Saint of Arse-lickers

THE POLICEMAN

THE BRITISH POLICEMAN is the envy of the world. Whether he's telling someone the time, helping an old lady with her shopping or chasing a masked bank robber, we see him every day on the streets of our cities, towns and villages. He's as much a part of the traditional British scene as Westminster Abbey, the tower of Big Ben and himselves on bicycles, two by two. Unlike his intimidating, gun-toting foreign counterpart, our approach-able bobby does his job armed with nothing more than a friendly smile, his sense of fair play and a 2-foot long extendable steel baton. Not surprisingly, it's every little boy's dream to be a policeman when he grows up, and if he works hard at school and passes all his exams he'll probably go and do something else. But what's it like being a policeman? Here are just a few of the situations that an ordinary copper might meet during an ordinary day on the job....

VICTIMS of burglary are often deeply traumatised by the experience of having their homes broken into. Here, an elderly lady has dialled 999 after discovering that her house has been ransacked. The sharp-eyed Scenes of Crimes officer notices that the thieves have omitted to take a priceless antique clock, some valuable war medals and a biscuit tin of cash from the sideboard. He decides to take them home, where he can examine them carefully for clues. Realising that the homeowner would be distressed if she saw these precious pieces of evidence being removed from her house, he gets his colleague to distract her whilst he puts them in a holdall.

A POLICEMAN often relies on a mysterious sixth sense to tell him when a crime may have been committed. In this scene, a traffic patrolman has pulled over a passing car in order to make some routine enquiries. A young man driving a fancy motor wouldn't usually arouse suspicion, but there is something about this particular driver that makes the policeman suspect that he may be guilty of an offence. The driver is asked to produce his documents. His insurance and MOT certificates are all in order and a quick check with the police computer proves he is the legitimate owner of the vehicle. But alarm bells are still ringing in the officer's head, so just to be on the safe side, the driver is tazered, taken back to the police station, roughed up, DNA-fingerprinted and held for 48 hours before being released without charge. He may have got away with whatever it might have been this time, but he knows that he'd better watch his step. The police are onto his little game, and they won't rest until they've got him safely behind bars for something.

WHETHER they are demonstrating against illegal wars, globalisation, or new laws that infringe civil rights, large groups of people often gather to exercise their right to protest. It is part of our country's proud, democratic tradition. But these troublemakers have to be kept under control and it is the police's job to maintain order, using force if necessary. Here a demo has turned ugly and a group of Tactical Support Group officers has had to move in to defuse a potential riot.

THE FIGHT against crime entered the technological age many years ago. These days, as much detective work is done behind a computer terminal as out on the street. Thanks to the police's massive database, few offenders can hope to hide from the long arm of the law for long. Here, a copper uses a car registration number to look up the home address of a driver, as a favour for a friend who has been cut up in traffic. The miscreant will later receive a late night visit from his victim, and a lesson in road manners that will hopefully make him think twice in future about the correct use of his indicators.

PAPERWORK makes up a large part of a modern bobby's duties. Filling in forms and writing cases up consumes many valuable hours that would be better spent out on the beat, fighting real criminals. Here, a man is being interviewed about a serious crime which has been committed. It would obviously be impractical to write down his words as he says them, so to save time the officers get him to sign several blank statement sheets first, adding his words afterwards when he is safely back in the cells. This creative approach to transcribing interviews saves a huge amount of police time, leads to a much higher crime clear-up rate, and has the added benefit of enabling trials to be completed much more quickly.

DRUNKENNESS is one of the most common criminal offences that our police have to deal with. However, arresting and prosecuting people who have had a few drinks too many on a night out is not always the best way to deal with the problem. Here, a pair of bobbies who are stationed in a busy town centre at closing time have taken a couple of tipsy young ladies into the back of their van to give them a good hard talking to about the importance of drinking sensibly.

X-RAY

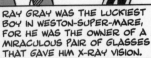

RAY GRAY WAS THE LUCKIEST BOY IN WESTON-SUPER-MARE, FOR HE WAS THE OWNER OF A MIRACULOUS PAIR OF GLASSES THAT GAVE HIM X-RAY VISION.

ONE MORNING.

TSK! TSK! I DON'T KNOW WHAT THE WORLD'S COMING TO.

WHAT IS IT, DEAR?

ANOTHER CELEBRITY GANG HAS HELD UP THE BANK.

DAILY RAG — 'STARS' HEIST AT LOCAL BA— POLICE BAFFLED

WHO WAS IT THIS TIME, DAD?

TERRY WOGAN AND DAVID BECKHAM.

COR!

AND MADONNA WAS DRIVING THE GETAWAY CAR.

THAT'S THE TENTH HOLD-UP IN A FORTNIGHT. AND ALL CELEBRITIES.

IT'S ALL MOST PECULIAR. YOU WOULDN'T THINK THEY WOULD NEED THE MONEY, WOULD YOU?

YOU WOULDN'T.

WHY DON'T THE POLICE ARREST THEM?

THEY CAN'T, RAY. WHEN THE ROBBERY OCCURRED, MADONNA WAS DOING A CONCERT AT THE HOLLYWOOD BOWL, WOGAN WAS ON THE RADIO AND BECKHAM WAS PLAYING FOR REAL MADRID AGAINST BARCELONA. BETWEEN THEM, THEY'VE GOT 30 MILLION WITNESSES TO SAY THEY WEREN'T IN WESTON-SUPER-MARE HIGH STREET.

GOSH!

LATER.

WA-HEY! TIME FOR A BIT OF FUN WITH MY X-RAY SPECS!

HEH-HEH! THESE GLASSES WERE THE BEST £1.25 I EVER SPENT!

BUT AS THE NUNS PASSED BY...

PHWOOOAR!... WHAT THE!?!...

I DON'T BELIEVE IT! ELVIS AND MR BEAN ARE HOLDING UP THE BANK! IT'S ANOTHER CELEBRITY ROBBERY.

JORDAN'S DRIVING THE GETAWAY CAR!

DING-A-LING-ALING-A-LING!

BANK

DID YOU SEE THAT? ELVIS, MR BEAN AND JORDAN (REAL NAME KATIE PRICE) JUST ROBBED THE BANK!

I DIDN'T SEE ANYTHING.

VROOM!